World Beneath the Sea

By JAMES DUGAN
ROBERT C. COWEN, BILL BARADA,
LUIS MARDEN, *and* RICHARD M. CRUM

Foreword by GILBERT M. GROSVENOR, *Associate Editor*
NATIONAL GEOGRAPHIC MAGAZINE

Prepared by Special Publications Division, ROBERT L. BREEDEN, *Chief*

NATIONAL GEOGRAPHIC SOCIETY, WASHINGTON, D. C.
MELVIN M. PAYNE, *President*
MELVILLE BELL GROSVENOR, *Editor-in-Chief;* FREDERICK G. VOSBURGH, *Editor*

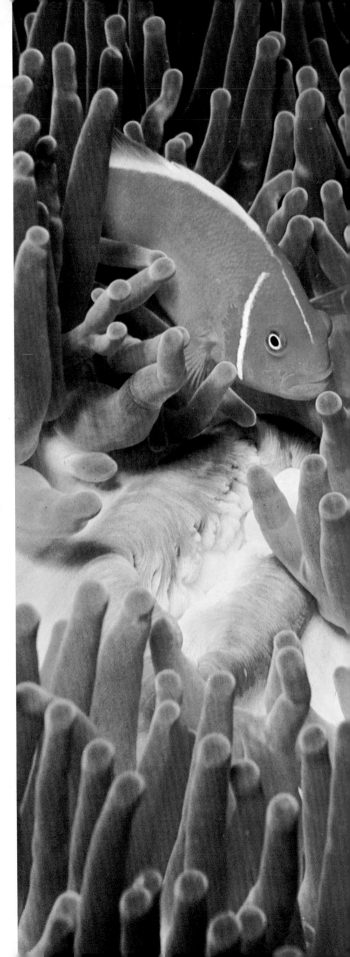

WORLD BENEATH THE SEA
BY JAMES DUGAN
ROBERT C. COWEN, BILL BARADA,
LUIS MARDEN, AND RICHARD M. CRUM

Published by
THE NATIONAL GEOGRAPHIC SOCIETY
MELVIN M. PAYNE, *President*
MELVILLE BELL GROSVENOR, *Editor-in-Chief*
FREDERICK G. VOSBURGH, *Editor*
GILBERT M. GROSVENOR,
   Executive Editor for this series

Volume Two of the second series of National
Geographic Books from the Special Publications Division.

ROBERT L. BREEDEN, *Editor*
DONALD J. CRUMP, *Associate Editor*
PHILIP B. SILCOTT, *Manuscript Editor*
TADD FISHER, *Project Editor*
THEODORE S. AMUSSEN, DAVID R. BRIDGE,
   MARY ANN HARRELL, GERALD S. SNYDER,
   Assistant Project Editors
JOHANNA G. FARREN, *Research and Style*
LOUISE GRAVES, TEE LOFTIN SNELL, JANE
   STEIN, PEGGY WINSTON, *Research*
LINDA M. SEEMAN, *Illustrations Research*
WAYNE BARRETT, RONALD M. FISHER, LOUISE
   GRAVES, WILLIAM R. GRAY, JR., DAVID
   MALLORY, GERALD S. SNYDER, *Picture Legends*
LUBA BALKO, MARGARET S. DEAN, CHRISTINE
   J. SCHWARTZ, *Production-Editorial Assistants*

Illustrations and Design

DAVID R. BRIDGE, *Picture Editor*
JOSEPH A. TANEY, *Art Director*
JOSEPHINE B. BOLT, *Assistant Art Director*

Production and Printing

RONALD M. FISHER, *Production*
JAMES R. WHITNEY, *Engraving and Printing*
JOHN R. METCALFE, *Assistant,*
   Engraving and Printing

*Living among stinging tentacles of a sea
anemone, a three-inch skunk clownfish
attracts larger prey for its host and in turn
eats leftovers. Overleaf: Sunlit air bubbles
dance past a branch of elkhorn coral as a
diver off the Florida coast enters the cap-
tivating world beneath the sea.*

CHAMBERED NAUTILUS, APPROXIMATELY 1/4 LIFE-SIZE (PAGE ONE)
DOUGLAS FAULKNER, PAGE ONE AND RIGHT; JERRY GREENBERG, OVERLEAF

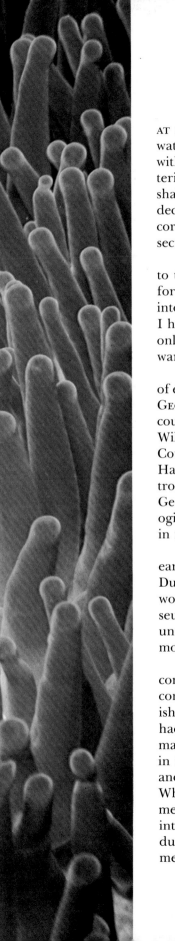

Foreword

AT LONG LAST, man has begun intensive exploration of his underwater world. The oceans, despite their great hazards, beguile him with their extravagant bounty. For centuries man probed the mysteries of the sea, venturing upon it in frail ships or exploring its shallows in crude diving machines. But only in the past three decades has he begun to study the depths with his own eyes. From coral reefs, and even down to the dark abysses, he is uncovering secrets nature has guarded for millions of years.

As one addicted to the sea, I can attest that a diver's attraction to the ocean floor is even more compelling than the sailor's love for open water. To this day, a decade later, I vividly recall diving into the Aegean Sea to pry loose some fragments of red pottery I had spotted from the surface. I retrieved no gold, no statuary, only barnacle-encrusted shards, but I carried away the most rewarding prize of all—the excitement of discovery.

You, as members of the Society, have shared this excitement of exploring the unknown seas through the pages of the NATIONAL GEOGRAPHIC. Since 1888, the Society has published numerous accounts of many adventurous men of this ocean era—men like Dr. William Beebe, first naturalist to enter the abyss; Jacques-Yves Cousteau, the intrepid French pioneer of the Aqua-Lung; Dr. Harold E. Edgerton, developer of deep-sea cameras and the electronic flash; Edwin A. Link, inventor and undersea explorer; George F. Bass and Peter Throckmorton, underwater archeologists. With the Society's support, they have won major victories in man's conquest of the mysterious sea.

When the Society decided to publish this book about the earth's last frontier, one author came immediately to mind: James Dugan, perhaps the world's foremost chronicler of the undersea world and its heroes. I first met Jim in the Oceanographic Museum in Monaco in 1962. There I listened eagerly to his tales of underwater explorers. Jim had followed closely the earliest to the most recent advances in diving and oceanography.

Tragically, James Dugan died at sea on June 1, 1967, before completing his manuscript for this volume. Although it cannot console those of us he left behind, Jim died doing what he cherished most: writing about the sea he loved. Those chapters he had completed reveal his great satisfaction in knowing that as man races toward the stars he still finds new challenges deep within the oceans of his own planet. Today, as I reread these pages and think of Jim, I remember one of his favorite poems: Walt Whitman's "Song for All Seas, All Ships," which was read at a memorial service for Jim. It praises "all brave captains and all intrepid sailors and mates, And all that went down doing their duty." To the last Jim was working at the task he defined for all men of the sea: "to expand human knowledge and wonder."

Gilbert M. Grosvenor

Contents

*In a coral glade off Isla de Cozumel, Mexico, an
amateur diver 70 feet down gathers swaying sea fans.*
BOB HOLLIS

1

Exploring the Ocean World

BY JAMES DUGAN

Pacific breaker explodes in a geyser of water against the coast of Hawaii. Earth's restless oceans — actually one vast interconnected sea — flood seven-tenths of the globe. For centuries man knew little more than the surface; now he has begun to explore the innermost depths.

INSIDE THE MINIATURE SUBMARINE, we lay on our stomachs peering through portholes into a slowly darkening world. As the Mediterranean Sea closed over us, the light dimmed from golden on the sunlit surface to aquamarine, and then to smoky green.

"Diving Saucer Mission number 402, October 4, 1965," my companion reported to the tape recorder logging our voyage. "Pilot, Albert Falco, *Observateur*, Jimmy Dugan. *Destination, Précontinent Trois.*"

Falco steered a roundabout course to a submerged outpost — Jacques-Yves Cousteau's Continental Shelf Station (Conshelf) Three — 328 feet down, off Cap Ferrat along the coast of southern France. In that sea-floor house six of my friends had lived and worked for 12 days without surfacing.

"Oceanauts," Cousteau dubbed this new breed of undersea technicians, members of a small international vanguard pioneering the occupation of the continental shelves. Their historic efforts — requiring submission to unremitting cold and dependence upon exotic breathing-gas mixtures to keep alive in an environment inhospitable to earthmen — held great significance for the future.

The gently sloping continental shelves are the pedestals of the land masses, almost equal to Africa in total area and incredibly rich in foods, fuels, and minerals. Most important, on an average their outer edges lie only a little more than 600 feet beneath the surface, a depth well within reach of underwater explorers. The oceanauts were helping to perfect the kind of sea-floor residence that may soon shelter marine miners and farmers. I couldn't help comparing my Conshelf Three visit to dropping in on a group of hopeful, isolated California prospectors in 1850.

As Falco and I descended, I had no sense of movement and became engrossed in checking the depth gauge...50 feet... 100...150. It grew darker outside. At first glimpse the nether slope of Cap Ferrat seemed an illusion. Against its vague shape, I saw hundreds of white specks, tiny organisms, drifting upward outside the ports.

Locked into a small, snug planet, we

9

JAMES M. ROBINSON (ABOVE) AND MARC JASINSKI

Drifting freely and weightlessly, a diver explores sheer walls of a submarine canyon off the coast of Tunisia. Beyond him stretches earth's last real frontier—a dark three-dimensional wilderness of canyon deeps, abyssal plains, and enormous mountain ranges virtually unknown to man. At the threshold of the deep frontier an underwater adventurer (left) roams with camera, plastic sketch pad, and spear. Delicately hued reefs like this one in Hawaiian waters lure growing numbers of amateur divers into fantastic coral realms that begin only a few feet beneath the surface.

it, peering into it, prowling its beaches, and once, protestingly, I probed its restless shallows when Falco coaxed me to put on an Aqua-Lung. Now I had become part of this liquid biospace that bulks three hundred times larger than our accustomed terrestrial environment.

Of all the planets in our solar system, earth alone is known to contain oceans—and earth's oceans are actually one vast sea. This water nourishes life; without it, we would quickly perish. Fossils more than two and a half billion years old indicate that from the womb of the salty sea emerged the beginnings of all life on earth.

This world ocean, this vast culture broth and spring of life, blankets seven-tenths of the globe and shrouds awesomely spectacular topography. But soundings and electronic magic, rather than personal inspection, have revealed most of the little we know about the grandeur of the depths.

I saw how these revelations came about while cruising with Cousteau on his oceanographic research ship *Calypso* during one of his Indian Ocean expeditions. I remember how the ship steamed along, singing the song of sonar—high-pitched pings strung in hypnotic series, each note projected toward the bottom of the sea and caught on the rebound. The time interval between ping and echo measured the distance the sound had passed through water. Fascinated, I watched the recording sonar as its stylus mysteriously sketched on graph paper the contour of the slope 2,700 feet down.

But these sketches form mere shadows

coasted through a marine Milky Way. As I lolled beside the imperturbable master of the three-dimensional voyage, I realized a wonderfully happy moment in my life. Only the whisper of the air-circulating system broke the silence. The extra pinch of oxygen doled to us increased my euphoria.

The sea had long been my companion, but never so intimately as this. I had spent much of my life sailing on it, writing about

THE AUTHOR: *"The sea imposes a modesty on those who try her," wrote James Dugan in 1956, and when he died on June 1, 1967, while writing this book, the sea's mysteries still captivated him. In 1944 he met Capt. Jacques-Yves Cousteau and began a collaboration that produced* The Living Sea. *He also wrote the narration for Cousteau's two Oscar-winning films,* The Silent World *and* World Without Sun. *His other books:* The Great Iron Ship, Man Under the Sea, American Viking, *and* The Great Mutiny.

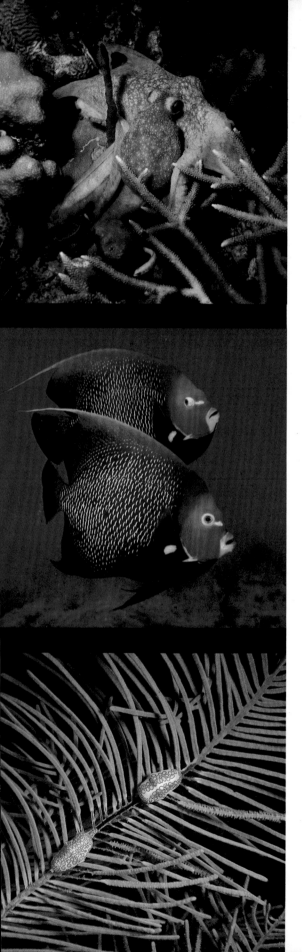

of reality. Most of the underwater canyons, trenches, valleys, mountains, and plains remain a territory not yet invaded by human explorers. And what a territory! Falco and I now lingered on the edge of this vast undersea world that covers more than 139 million square miles and contains superlative geography.

Earth's longest mountain range, the Mid-Oceanic Ridge, meanders between the continental land masses for 35,000 miles through all the oceans. Rising 6,000 to 12,000 feet above the bottom, the pinnacles of the ridge occasionally break through the surface to form islands, such as the Azores and Ascension. In expanse, the ridge almost matches the area of all the continents.

Although 29,028-foot Mount Everest is the roof of the land above the water, earth's greatest known height has its roots in the Pacific off Peru. There the Andes ascend 25,000 feet before surfacing, then climb another 23,000 feet—a total rise of more than nine miles.

The deep trenches claim my admiration most of all, for they have no rivals on dry land. In 1960, the bathyscaph *Trieste* carried two observers down nearly seven miles into the Mariana Trench in the Pacific— the farthest penetration made by man into the deepest known place in the ocean.

Unfortunately, bathyscaphs lack mobility; they serve best as marine elevators. And the more mobile conventional submarines are not designed for reaching great depths. Considering these facts, I realized I was reclining in a 21st-century sea craft. Already, descendants of the

Filming marvels of a coral reef off the Florida Keys, a photographer uses a ring-shaped flash reflector around the lens for close-ups of a convoluted brain coral. Tiny wrasses flit past unafraid. Its tentacles draped on staghorn coral, a briar octopus lurks to grab mollusks and crustaceans. French angelfish bear sharp cheek barbs that can stab an attacker. Spotted flamingo tongues graze on an undulating sea fan.

JERRY GREENBERG (OPPOSITE); JAMES DUTCHER (CENTER); AND DOUGLAS FAULKNER
APPROXIMATE SIZES: OCTOPUS 1/2 LIFE-SIZE; ANGELFISH
1/6 LIFE-SIZE; FLAMINGO TONGUES 1/2 LIFE-SIZE

13

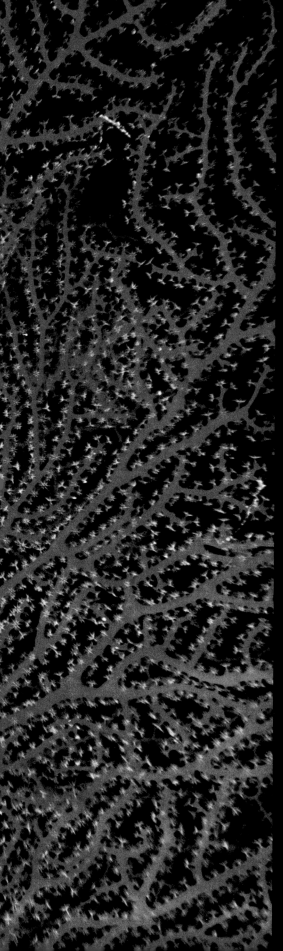

Lacy red sea fan (left), a colonial animal, sieves plankton through myriad tentacles. A vase sponge (above) draws food and oxygen through fine pores in its skin.

Swift, ferocious hunters, blackbarred jacks (above) school in warm seas. Mollusk without a shell, the Spanish Dancer sea slug (below) glides above shelf coral.

highly maneuverable diving saucer were performing tasks far in excess of her depth capacity of 1,100 feet.

Shortly after Cousteau tested his first saucer in 1959, the overjoyed inventor wrote: "...already I can see that this odd jet-propelled vehicle will let us fulfill a dream: to descend deeper and stay longer than the free diver can, while still being able to move, look about, and even pick things up. This is revolutionary. The way opens for geological and biological research in a marine twilight zone no man could explore freely before."

Now Falco and I were roaming that zone, that mysterious realm "teeming, beckoning, unexplored," as Cousteau had put it. Our saucer could make little more than half a knot, but the clamlike craft glided about almost as easily as a fish. Two battery-powered hydrojet nozzles propelled us and controlled our direction. When Falco pointed the nozzles down, jets of water thrust the saucer up. When he pointed them up, we went down. To turn left, he used the power of the right nozzle only. To turn right, he used the left nozzle.

Actually, Falco had let the craft drift downward without power until we reached 270 feet. Then he turned on the jets and began putting the saucer through her acrobatic paces as he unerringly flitted about in the dark, prolonging our excursion.

Intruder in a strange animal kingdom crouches behind a jagged outcrop of living coral. Beside her sprout a vase sponge and a branching sea whip. Long mistaken for plants and stones, corals grow in all the seas, but reef-building varieties flourish only in tropic shallows. Cellulose-like stalked tunicates cluster in a colony (center). Anchoring themselves to twigs of coral or submerged rocks, these twin-mouthed creatures filter food from water drawn into one siphon and squirted out of the other. The sea anemone (bottom) often paralyzes fish with hypodermic filaments, then draws its prey into an inner sac. With its false eye, the golden longnosed butterfly-fish confuses attackers that find it hard to tell whether their quarry is coming or going.

BOB MARCUCCI (TOP); LEROY FRENCH (CENTER); NATE LAWRENCE (BOTTOM); AND DOUGLAS FAULKNER. APPROXIMATE SIZES: STALKED TUNICATES 2/3 LIFE-SIZE; SEA ANEMONE 1/3 LIFE-SIZE; BUTTERFLY-FISH 1 1/7 LIFE-SIZE

16

He flipped a switch and the submarine's exterior lights blazed a trail through the water. The sea came alive. I saw a circus of color: red gorgonians, yellow sponges, and purple sea urchins on greenish-gray corals. Small fish pranced unafraid in the sudden brightness. An octopus sprawled on a sandy ridge. And all around us swarmed a host of tiny creatures—jellyfish, worms, crustaceans, and the young of crabs, lobsters, and fishes.

Falco gaily revolved the jets to swoop and climb. Then he reversed the flow to slow down and we hovered beside the reef. Cousteau had told me that despite the saucer's grunting and whining when under power, it did not frighten fish away, but attracted them instead. I wondered if they saw the submersible as an engaging clown of a clam, a great yellow clam with staring, curious eyes that refused to stay put on the bottom where it belonged.

We zoomed downward and began to glide over the bottom. I was completely disoriented. I guessed our direction as northwest, but the compass needle indicated east by southeast. Falco pressed on as confidently as a householder in the dusk of his own backyard.

"*Regardez la grosse langouste,*" he said. I didn't see any big lobster. Seconds later it came into the arena of light, waving long antennae. My pilot had seen it beyond in the gloom. Turning to starboard, Falco skimmed above a cluster of gesturing

Drained of water, the ocean beds emerge as a spectacular region unrivaled by anything on land. Towering peaks, plunging canyons, and plains flat as tabletops remain undisturbed by erosion of wind and rain. Ships' echo sounders mapped this underwater world, bouncing electronic signals off the bottom, measuring the time between pings, then automatically charting depth profiles. The Mid-Oceanic Ridge, crisscrossed with fracture zones and grooved by a rift valley, winds for 35,000 miles through all of earth's oceans. On either side, broad basins and plains stretch to the shallow continental shelves.

PAINTING BY HEINRICH C. BERANN BASED ON BATHYMETRIC STUDIES BY BRUCE C. HEEZEN AND MARIE THARP OF THE LAMONT GEOLOGICAL OBSERVATORY

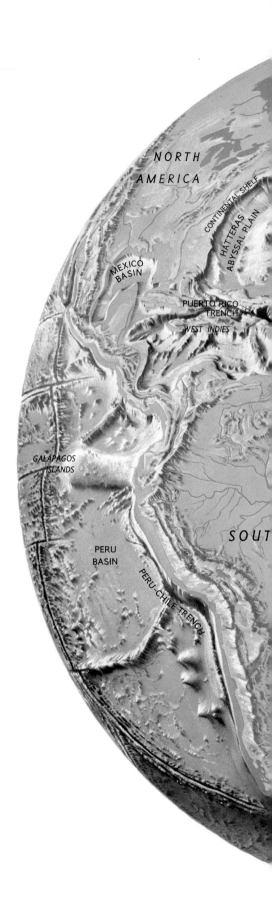

lobsters and climbed full jet, telling me about a scorpionfish that lived up the hill.

"Voilà! La scorpène." I saw nothing. "Right there," he pointed. "Don't you see him?" Again my land-oriented eyes failed to detect anything—the weedy coloration of the scorpionfish blended with its background. But Falco swung the saucer to within a foot of it, and I caught a glimpse of an eye and the outline of the mouth just before the fish stirred and whipped away.

Falco settled the saucer on a muddy plain covered with a tangle of rubber air hoses and power and communication cables. Something thumped on our steel hull, but Falco volunteered no explanation for the noise. Quickly he spun us around, simultaneously extending the hydraulic claw the saucer keeps clenched under her bow except when gathering samples. So neatly done that it betrayed rehearsal, an oceanaut shook hands with the saucer.

Through his face mask, I recognized the mischievous brown eyes of André Laban, mission chief of Conshelf Three. A black rubber suit with yellow tapes on the seams sheathed him from head to foot. His breathing hoses curled away into the murk. André, like the other oceanauts, inhaled "heliox," a mixture of helium and oxygen pumped to them from the undersea house when they worked outside. Without this special pressurized gas mixture, the menfish could not survive for long. At such a

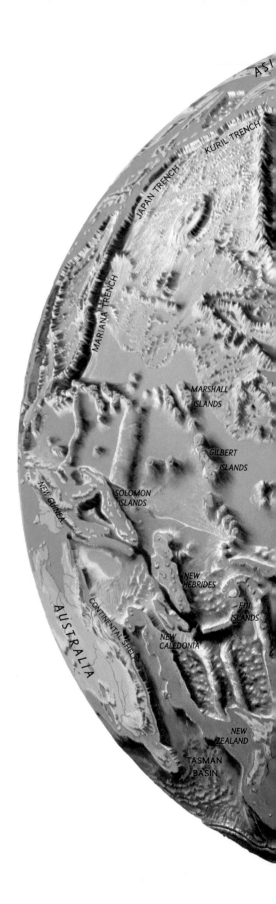

Covering almost one-third of the globe, the Pacific could swallow the seven continents. The Mariana Trench reaches earth's greatest known depth, nearly seven miles below the surface of the sea. If placed beside Mount Everest, Hawaii's highest peak, rising 32,024 feet from the sea floor, would spire more than half a mile above the Himalayan giant. Walls of the fracture zones climb as much as 10,500 feet. Skirting Antarctica, the Mid-Oceanic Ridge continues its sweep around the world. The rift valley, 30 miles wide in places, leads some scientists to believe the earth is splitting open along the globe-girdling crevasse and growing larger—but at an infinitesimal rate.

PAINTING BY HEINRICH C. BERANN BASED ON BATHYMETRIC STUDIES BY BRUCE C. HEEZEN AND MARIE THARP OF THE LAMONT GEOLOGICAL OBSERVATORY

depth, the air we breathe on the surface would become highly dangerous because of its nitrogen content.

Two more oceanauts swam into our lights, and beyond them I caught my first glimpse of Conshelf Three. Nineteen feet across, the great black-and-yellow-checkered sphere rested like a forgotten beach ball on a chassis holding 77 tons of ballast. The steel house contained two stories, the lower for diving, sleeping, and sanitation, the upper for dining, communications, and sorting the many samples gathered from the sea floor.

In a happy salute to our friends, Falco glided up and over the sphere and brushed between two cylindrical escape chambers

on the chassis, each kept under pressure to carry the oceanauts to the surface in an emergency. He climbed above the house and then dived toward it, pulling up as I closed my eyes for the crash. Once he put the bow down so hard that my face flattened painfully against the porthole.

Falco enjoyed this noodling around. I knew he rarely could joyride in the saucer. Almost always he transports a scientist or an engineer with fixed designs on a particular spot for observation. Then poor Falco acts as a chauffeur. Today he swooped and swerved like a stunt pilot.

As the bow shot up again, I saw an overhang of yellow steel plate directly above us and in it a shimmering round mirror of water—the always-open hatch of the undersea station. Water never rises above the hatch, because the heliox pressure inside equals the water pressure outside. Falco had expertly slipped the saucer between the uprights supporting the sphere, putting us under the hatch with no more than two or three feet to spare.

He circled the house again. It was about breakfast time, Falco said, time for the oceanauts to be downing their usual beakers of *café au lait* and hunks of bread smeared with jam, chestnut puree, and chocolate. Such a thing would have been pure hallucination a quarter of a century ago when I first became addicted to following man's struggle with the sea.

Those 25 years—especially the last ten—witnessed more progress in underwater exploration than all the years before. For centuries, none save divers for pearls, coral,

JERRY GREENBERG

Sea Scooter, its twin screws driven by electric motors, tows developer Carl Gage above a coral garden off Key Largo, Florida. The scooter can take him silently to depths of 100 feet and pull him for three hours at speeds up to three knots. Sawing into the metal of a sunken ship, a diver wears a cryogenic lung that converts supercooled liquid oxygen and nitrogen (at −318° F.) into a breathable gas by piping it through warming coils. Designed by Floridian Jim Woodberry, the rig allows its user to stay down more than six hours.

Pushing through a "skylight" of ice, the U.S. nuclear submarine Skate surfaces 300 miles from the North Pole. Comdr. James F. Calvert took this remarkable photograph on March 22, 1959.

Diving saucer designed by French Navy Capt. Jacques-Yves Cousteau encounters Aqua-Lungers six fathoms deep in the Red Sea.

Underwater runabout: Propeller-driven Italian submersible gives divers a lift, sparing their muscles and extending their range.

shellfish and sponges had firsthand knowledge of the contents of Neptune's domain. Dependent upon their ability to hold their breath, they could go on inspection tours of only a minute or two and cover sharply limited areas.

The desire for trade and new lands motivated many of our ancestors to venture on harrowing surface voyages. But for centuries even the saltiest old salts trembled at the thought of terrors awaiting them should they be unfortunate enough to "go below." Only the steady advance of scientific discovery eventually routed their fears—among them, the belief that frightful monsters skulked in the deep.

I MAGINE, if you can, a beast a mile and a half in circumference and covered with seaweed. The Norwegians believed it existed, and passed down stories about it from one generation to the next. The kraken, as they called this biggest of all creatures, continued to seize and swallow prey until the early 19th century. Not until then did it die in the minds of its believers.

Other imagined monsters included lobsters huge enough to drag down sailors with their claws and serpents that crushed whole ships in their coils. If seafarers managed to escape these horrors, they undoubtedly thought themselves more vulnerable to the songs of silken-haired sea nymphs with a single mission: to lure sailors to their death.

Hazards real and imagined failed to daunt a scattering of daring visionaries who persisted through the ages with experiments calculated to offer men safe passage into the sea. Instead of myth, these farsighted, fearless innovators bequeathed new knowledge to those who succeeded them.

Conshelf Three and similar stations prove that man can inhabit, not merely visit, earth's last real frontier. "We have heeded our own discoveries and learned the lessons they present," Cousteau said of Conshelf Three. "The greatest of these is that if man is to make an undersea creature of himself, he must do it wholeheartedly and without a backward glance. As with a newborn infant, the umbilical cord must be severed.

"We are confident," Cousteau continued, "that within a few years we will entirely eliminate ties to the world above. Then, for the first time, oceanauts will have true freedom of the deep."

Such freedom, I thought, will allow chemists to set up shop in a sea-bottom laboratory. Biologists will revel in the study of fabulous beings as yet unseen. Botanists will stroll underwater gardens; geologists will decipher the history of the world ocean laid down in silt, sand, mud, and rock. There will be room here, too, for philosophers, poets, and artists.

"Time to go back," Falco said, and I faced the inevitable end of my extraordinary voyage. After dropping the ascent ballast, he muttered final entries into the log, and we climbed aloft. In hundreds of surfacings, Falco has emerged neither so near the mother ship that he imperils his craft nor so far away that he is ever out of sight of her.

Faint green light appeared and grew golden as the sun sparkled in the ports once more. Outside, a crewman made fast a line to haul us into range of the tackle that a few minutes later lifted the saucer into its cradle. I extended my arm up through the hatch and cleared my other shoulder through. Before me spread the familiar shores of France, gleaming in the winy October sun, but mentally I lingered in the hidden realm of the depth men. Falco and I had returned from a morning in the future.

Undersea house and workshop, Continental Shelf Station Three rests 328 feet down in the Mediterranean. Here six oceanauts stayed three weeks, leaving the steel sphere daily to carry out their assigned tasks. Hovering near the upper hatch, a crew member checks for rust and damage to power and communication cables. At the surface Captain Cousteau, director of the $700,000 project, kept constant vigil by television monitor as the team boldly advanced man's ability to live and work in the sea.

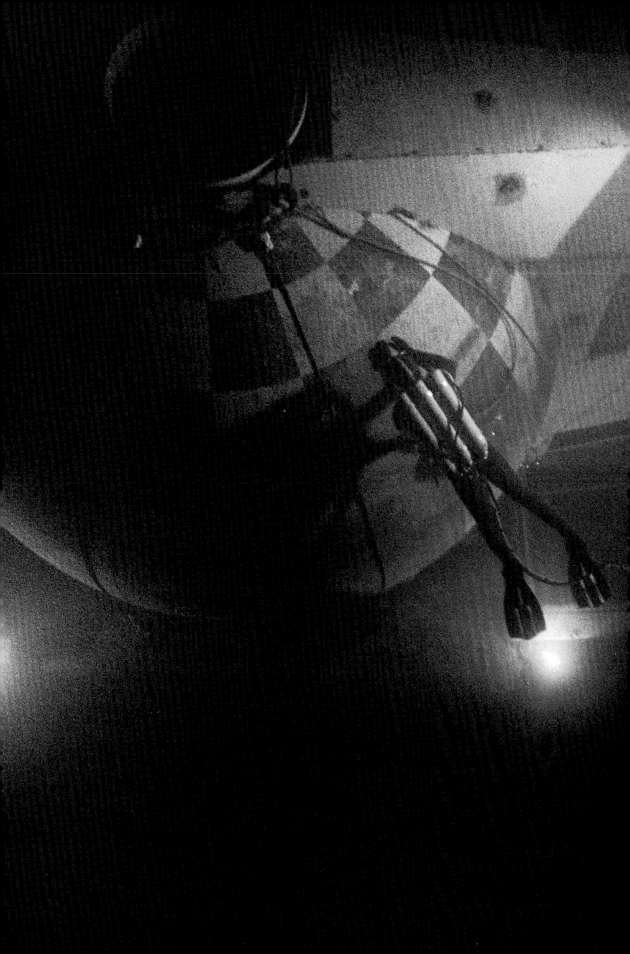

2

Man Invades the Sea

BY JAMES DUGAN

Mysteries of the underwater world lure Alexander the Great, King of Macedonia. Legend says he entered the sea in a "barrel" or "cage" of glass in the 4th century B.C. An unknown artist painted this miniature 2,000 years later in India.

MORE THAN FOUR CENTURIES AGO two adventurous Greeks, each carrying a lighted candle, hoisted themselves into what looked like a huge upended vase and entered the depths of the River Tagus at Toledo, Spain. Taut ropes lowered their ungainly apparatus while lead weights kept it from tilting and pulled it toward the bottom. No one knows how long they stayed underwater, but an eyewitness wrote that they emerged unharmed — with the candles still burning.

Thousands of spectators crowded the riverbanks that memorable day in 1538; many must have thought uneasily of sorcery. But in fact they were watching an exhibition of a primitive diving bell, staged before Charles V of Spain, ruler of the Holy Roman Empire. The two Greeks, dry and comfortable, breathed air trapped inside their crude submersible.

Their descent, one of the earliest reported with any detail and accuracy, drew attention to the diving bell, already an ancient but little-known device, and its use in salvage work on sunken ships spread slowly throughout Europe. Man was taking a long step into that dark underwater world that had fascinated him for thousands of years.

The sea itself, almost literally, is in man's blood, for the fluid that courses our bodies is much like seawater in chemical composition. Yet for us the oceans are a hostile environment. And the dangers increase with depth because the weight of water exerts great pressure on anything in it.

Today we can build submarines that hold this pressure out. Their crewmen live in an atmosphere like the air we breathe every day. In the diving saucer, for example, Falco and I carried a bit of our surface world down with us. Undersea observation chambers like the bathysphere and the bathyscaph give men the same protection. So do the clumsy experimental suits of metal that amount to wraparound submarines. This kind of packaged safety is fairly new in our invasion of the sea.

Ancient diving bells, on the other hand, and now undersea stations like Conshelf Three represent victories man has won in adapting his body to underwater pressure.

Man probably took his earliest steps into the sea in search of food. And what courage those first dives must have required! Imagine the boldest of the seashore tribesmen wading past minnows that skittered in the shallows, learning to paddle, swimming beyond the surf, and staring down through wavering green light. Finally, taking a deep breath, they ventured into a new world—a world where strange creatures darted and slithered among the rocks, where fearful dangers might lie just out of sight in the murk, or in the crevices of a coral reef.

Eventually men learned to wrest wealth from beneath the waves. Divers played an important role in the ancient world. Greeks and Romans worked in a thriving sponge industry, and their harvest had uses that seem strange today. Dipped in honey, sponges pacified babies; soaked in water, they became soldiers' canteens.

War provided still another reason for going underwater. In the 5th century B.C. when King Xerxes futilely attempted to conquer Greece, part of his fleet lay at anchor off Mount Pelion. Suddenly a severe storm struck without warning. The celebrated diver Scyllias and his daughter Hydna, who had deserted the Persian king and taken up the Greek cause, plunged into the waves. They swiftly began cutting anchor ropes, and the storm played havoc with the enemy ships.

Breath-holding divers still forage for treasure in many parts of the world—Japan, Korea, North Africa, Polynesia. In the Persian Gulf, I have sketched pearl hunters making lung-bursting dives as though special gear had never been invented. Holding stones to speed them down, they vanish in the turquoise water, snatching up oysters from the bottom, then rise gasping beside the boat, dark shoulders gleaming among vivid ripples in the savage heat. Yet even the most skilled of such "lung divers" can stay underwater only 90 seconds to two minutes at best, and they seldom go below 140 feet.

From Aristotle we get our first report of how man put his ingenuity to work to take air to divers under the surface. More than 2,000 years ago he wrote: "... they can give respiration to divers by letting down a bucket, for this does not fill with water, but retains its air. Its lowering has to be done by force." By swimming up into the large barrel-like containers and gulping a deep breath of the trapped air near the top, the divers could stay down longer.

And tales persist that in the 4th century B.C. Alexander the Great descended in what might have been a diving bell similar to an upended bucket. Though fables cloud the feats of the Macedonian king, it is highly possible that his courage and curiosity led him down into the sea. Legend says he rode in a "barrel" or "cage" of glass

BETTMANN ARCHIVE

Divers armed with compressed-air guns explore the eerie fantasy world created by Jules Verne in his book Twenty Thousand Leagues Under the Sea, *published in 1870. Their suits reflect gear invented five years earlier in France. Crewmen inside Verne's* Nautilus *gaze at a huge octopus.*

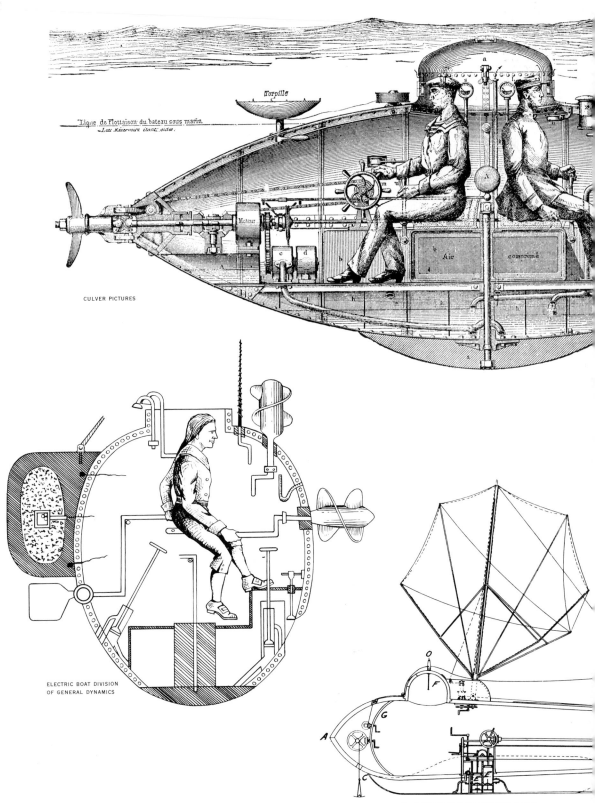

Torpille

Ligne de Flottaison du bateau sous marin.
Les Réservoirs étant vides.

Moteur

Air comprimé

CULVER PICTURES

ELECTRIC BOAT DIVISION
OF GENERAL DYNAMICS

FROM ORIGINAL PLANS OF ROBERT FULTON'S "NAUTILUS," 1798

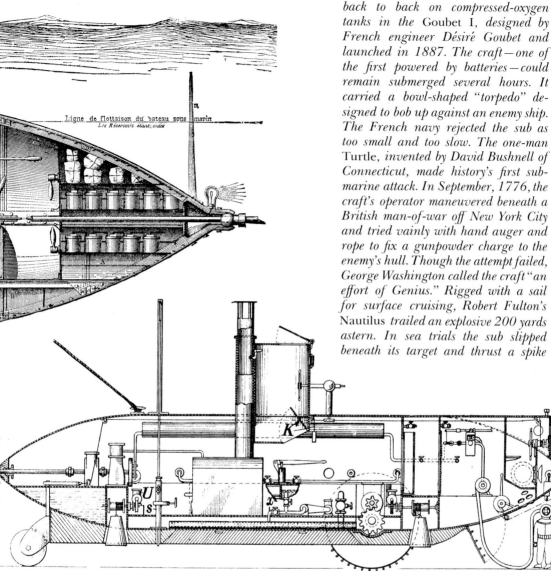

Ligne de flottaison du bateau sous marin
Les Réservoirs étant vides

ELECTRIC BOAT DIVISION OF GENERAL DYNAMICS

Early submarines: Two-man crew sits back to back on compressed-oxygen tanks in the Goubet I, designed by French engineer Désiré Goubet and launched in 1887. The craft — one of the first powered by batteries — could remain submerged several hours. It carried a bowl-shaped "torpedo" designed to bob up against an enemy ship. The French navy rejected the sub as too small and too slow. The one-man Turtle, invented by David Bushnell of Connecticut, made history's first submarine attack. In September, 1776, the craft's operator maneuvered beneath a British man-of-war off New York City and tried vainly with hand auger and rope to fix a gunpowder charge to the enemy's hull. Though the attempt failed, George Washington called the craft "an effort of Genius." Rigged with a sail for surface cruising, Robert Fulton's Nautilus trailed an explosive 200 yards astern. In sea trials the sub slipped beneath its target and thrust a spike

and ring into the planking. A cable, threaded through the ring, pulled the floating mine toward the vessel. Cross section of the ship's bottom (Q) shows the explosive (P) just before impact. France, Britain, and the United States spurned Fulton's underwater warship. Argonaut, with an air lock for sending out divers, crawled on cast-iron wheels. Intended for undersea exploration, the boat made its first descent in Maryland's Patapsco River in 1897, operated by inventor Simon Lake. Air hoses for venting the gasoline engine sharply limited Argonaut's depth.

Cranking the drive shaft, crewmen power the Confederate submarine Hunley *as the captain peers from the conning tower. The drawing exaggerates the size of the craft. Actually, she carried just nine men and had an inside height of only five feet. In an 1863 painting (top), soldiers guard the converted steam boiler in a Charleston, South Carolina, dry dock. The* Hunley *became the first submarine to sink a ship in war when she rammed a torpedo into the U.S.S.* Housatonic *in Charleston Harbor in 1864. But the explosion of the charge sent the sub to the bottom as well.*

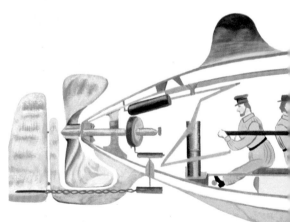

—a material, remarkably enough, that may form the hulls of future deep submergence vehicles, because its molecular structure resists compression stresses as the weight of the water increases.

With a drinking glass, you can easily make your own "diving bell." Turn the tumbler upside down, hold it level, and push it into water. If you are careful not to tip the glass, it will trap all the air inside, forming, in effect, a model of Alexander's cage. If you could push the tumbler several feet down, the air inside would be compressed, reduced in volume by the pressure of the water in the mouth of the glass.

In the ocean, a quart of air trapped at the surface will compress to a pint at 33 feet, half a pint at 100 feet—whether in an open bottle or in the human body. And this compressed air can be deadly to a diver. My friend Capt. George F. Bond, USN, a specialist in underwater medicine, once startled me by pointing out how easily it could have killed one of the men I most admire: English astronomer Edmond Halley, who explored both stars and sea.

In 1691 Halley patented a diving bell made of wood and coated with lead to make it sink. With no ill effects from the "condensed air," as he called it, Halley and four companions spent more than an hour and a half in the bell at about 60 feet.

"But if Halley had stayed at that depth just a few minutes longer," George explained, "he might have died when he came up. If such a famous man had been

lost in that kind of accident, the practice of diving could have suffered a severe setback."

No one understood then that a person breathing compressed air for an extended time below 39 feet risks paralysis and death unless "decompressed" before returning to the outside air. Early bell and helmet men usually worked short shifts in shallow water, and no doubt many of them escaped trouble by sheer good fortune.

Designs for diving helmets appeared

centuries ago. About 1500 Leonardo da Vinci sketched a helmeted figure breathing through a tube buoyed by a float at the surface. Anyone wearing such gear would have great difficulty—a man just four feet down could not draw air through the tube because his lungs could not overcome the external water pressure. But if compressed air could have been pumped into the helmet, it would have equalized the pressure and allowed the diver to breathe easily.

Credit for a reliable system of supplying compressed air to divers goes to Augustus Siebe, a German engineer who found England "an inventor's paradise" and settled there. He developed a "closed suit" made watertight by rubber cuffs and a collar. Divers liked his new apparatus because they could wear clothing under it and keep out the cold of the sea. The suit soon became standard, and today it serves as effectively as it did when he introduced it in 1837.

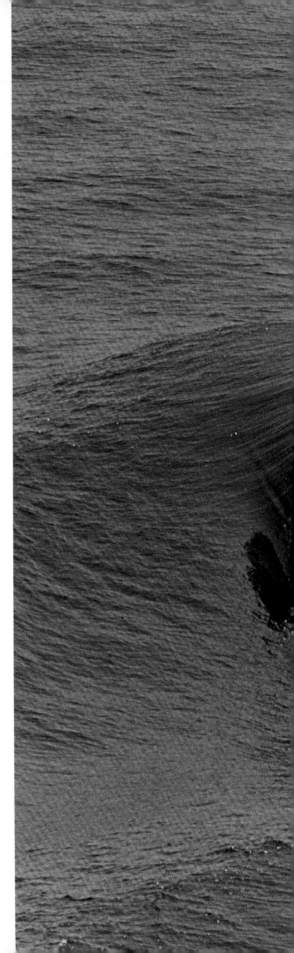

The same year one of the first diving-equipment firms in the United States, the presently named Morse Company of Boston, went into business. It's still going strong.

I visited the company's eighth-floor workshops on Sleeper Street, hard by Boston Harbor, and found a graying coppersmith making helmets with breastplates much as his fellow craftsmen had done a century before. I watched him hammer a copper disk around a steel form until it took shape as a breastplate, then solder on a neck ring for fastening it to the helmet. He fitted the helmet itself with a glass faceplate and three other windows, an air escape valve, and two goosenecks. The first would hold an air hose, the second a telephone line.

"We build them to last," said William P. Dugan, president of Morse's, as he smiled at my surprise over the unvarying art of helmet-making. "The other day a man brought in an old helmet for repair. We checked our files and found that we had sold it to his grandfather. Three generations have used it."

While the helmet-and-hose divers of the mid-1800's plodded about in the silt of harbors and riverbeds, compressed air found other uses. Workmen in caissons breathed it as they dug tunnels or sank bridge piers. Returning to the surface, both groups often showed the same symptoms: rashes and itching, choking, and agonizing pains in joints and muscles. Their bodies twisted into the dreaded bends that no doctor could relieve until a French physiologist, Paul Bert, discovered the cause.

An energetic and unorthodox man, Bert first investigated the effects of rarefied air on mountain climbers and balloonists. Then he turned his attention to other extremes of pressure, those of the world beneath the sea.

Roiling water cascades from diving planes on the fin of the nuclear submarine Shark *as it cruises in the Atlantic. Another atomic sub,* Triton, *circled the globe in 1960. Without surfacing, it logged 30,752 miles in 61 days.*

BURKE UZZLE

In 1878 he traced the torment of bends to its source—nitrogen breathed under pressure. This heavy inert gas makes up four-fifths of our atmosphere; as a rule it slips harmlessly in and out of our lungs. But a diver 33 feet down breathes twice as much nitrogen, at 66 feet three times as much. Pressure drives it into his blood and tissues. When a diver has absorbed all the gas his body will hold, he is "saturated."

As long as he remains under enough pressure—at saturation depth—the dissolved nitrogen causes no difficulty. If he comes up before too much of it accumulates, as Halley did, his lungs can get rid of it. But let him ascend too far too fast and the gas will cause his blood to start frothing like a well-shaken bottle of soda pop. The explosion of bubbles will clog the blood vessels, torturing, perhaps killing, him.

PAUL BERT BELIEVED that a diver could reach the surface in safety if hauled up slowly enough for his lungs to eliminate the excess gas from his body. From 100 feet, for example, an hour-long ascent would ward off the bends.

Divers learned they could relieve a victim of the malady by returning him to the water and hauling him up slowly. Or they could place the patient in an airtight chamber, put him back under an air pressure equal to his diving depth, and gradually reduce the pressure.

I have never seen anyone afflicted with the bends, but in Monaco my wife Ruth and I learned that an acquaintance, a young biologist, had survived the terrible ordeal. After five days' decompression treatment, the hospital had just released him. We couldn't get over how pinched and shrunken he looked.

"He actually seems physically smaller," Ruth remarked.

This phenomenon of saturation, which can prove so deadly to divers, led to the startling discovery that men can adapt themselves to pressure at a given depth and *live* underwater. All a diver needs is a sea-floor dwelling that he can enter and leave at will, with an inside atmosphere com-

pressed to equal the pressure of the surrounding water. George Bond suggested this concept of "saturation diving" in 1957, and men have since lived and worked in the sea for a month without surfacing.

The search for diving safety has long occupied scientists. In 1906 Professor John Scott Haldane of Scotland employed helmet-hose suits for refining Bert's discoveries into systematic decompression tables. Many years later I had the good fortune of meeting colleagues of Haldane in his historic research with the British Admiralty Deep Diving Committee. One, Guybon C. C. Damant, became a good friend. Much as he disliked publicity about his remarkable dives, he obligingly told me of his work as a young gunnery officer in the Royal Navy.

"Unlike most of my class of budding gunnery lieutenants," Damant said, "I found going underwater to be a delightful experience and infinitely preferred it to the study of ballistics and gun drill."

Haldane declared that divers could ascend faster than Bert had recommended, and, in fact, *should*—in stages. For instance, a diver 100 feet down would be hauled quickly to 50 feet and, after a stop there, rise to 25 feet for another stage of decompression, halving the pressure at each level. This way he would eliminate nitrogen faster and reach the surface sooner.

To test the theory, Damant and Gunner Andrew Y. Catto got into heavy helmet dress and dived from H.M.S. *Spanker* off the southwest coast of Scotland. The first day they descended to 138 feet, and later as deep as 180 feet. Each time they came up in stages—exhausted but without having the bends.

Finally, Lt. Damant and Mr. Catto

Diving bell patented in 1691 by English astronomer Edmond Halley enables salvors to recover sunken cannon. Weighted barrels take air down to the lead-coated wooden chamber. Halley also devised a technique of supplying air to helmet-hose divers, conveying it from the diving bell "in a continued stream by small, flexible pipes."

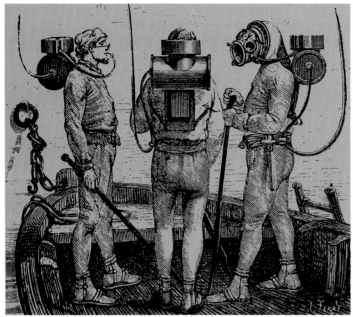

"Diving Armour," patented in America in 1830, resembles an oversized snorkel. No record exists that anyone ever built or tested the device.

Hoses and canisters supply air to divers preparing to submerge with Aérophores *developed in France in 1865 by mining engineer Benoît Rouquayrol and Navy Lt. Auguste Denayrouze. The reservoirs, filled with pressurized air, would give a diver several minutes to save himself*

if his air line parted. In 1680 Italian physicist Giovanni Borelli envisioned gear (below) that would free man from the surface, "purifying" its own air supply by passing it through a tube cooled by sea water. His concept included a hand-cranked ballast tank and clawlike foot fins.

volunteered to go below 200 feet, deeper than man had ever ventured before. "Mark you," Damant told me, "we were not attempting to set any records. We were simply trying to provide a greater working range for compressed-air diving."

For the unprecedented plunge, *Spanker* moved into deeper water, in Loch Striven. There Damant, then Catto, planted their lead boots on the bottom, 210 feet down. Their decompression stops completed, they surfaced without harm from a depth no other man would reach for nearly a decade.

The Committee's tables still form the basis of all compressed-air diving guides to prevent the bends. But the diver faces still another problem, the insidious danger of nitrogen narcosis—"rapture of the deep."

Nitrogen can intoxicate a diver almost like alcohol, and the effect increases with depth. I have often asked divers how it

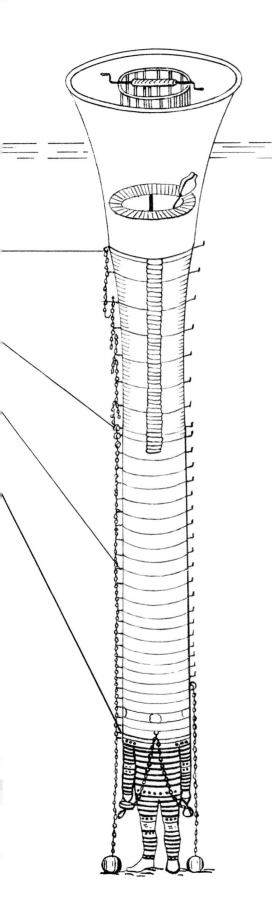

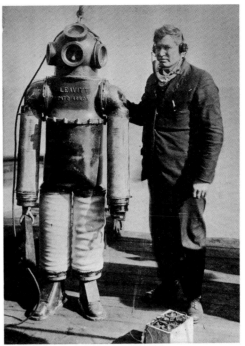

Hoping to salvage the Lusitania, *American diver Benjamin Leavitt (above) publicized a semi-armored suit in 1922. His plans failed for lack of funds. The boiler-shaped rig (below), built in Germany in 1797, allowed a diver to stay briefly in shallow water.*

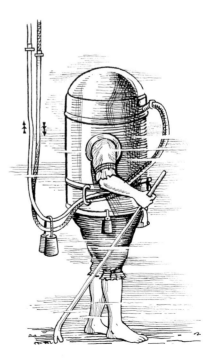

41

feels. Their answers jibe with Cousteau's:

"The first stage is a mild anesthesia, after which the diver becomes a god. If a passing fish seems to require air, the crazed diver may tear out his air pipe or mouth grip as a sublime gift."

Difficulties with compressed air led to the testing of other breathable mixtures. One is the helium-oxygen that oceanauts used at Conshelf Three, and hydrogen-oxygen another. But these combinations carry hazards of their own.

If too much oxygen is added to hydrogen, the mixture becomes highly explosive. Helium averts narcosis but causes rapid loss of body heat in cold water and distorts the shivering diver's speech into a high-pitched garble. In spite of these drawbacks, however, helium seems the best choice.

Men underwater have long relied on simple signals to the surface, tugging at hose or rope by prearranged code. The invention of the telephone provided some with a more sophisticated communication system. But lines can snag on rocks and wreckage and trap the man they protect. Only by breaking these tethers could divers move about with ease.

Attempts to free men from all dependence on the surface began centuries ago. Leonardo sketched a design for an underwater costume with a "breastplate of armour," sacks of sand for ballast, and a "wine-skin to contain the breath" — the first serious effort to devise self-contained underwater breathing equipment.

Almost 200 years later, another Italian, Giovanni Borelli, tried to extend the diver's range with more complex gear. He believed exhaled air could be purified and breathed again if simply channeled through a copper tube cooled by sea water so condensation in the tube would trap "impurities."

His insight outran the technology of his day. For years specialists rejected his concept as one that couldn't possibly work. But

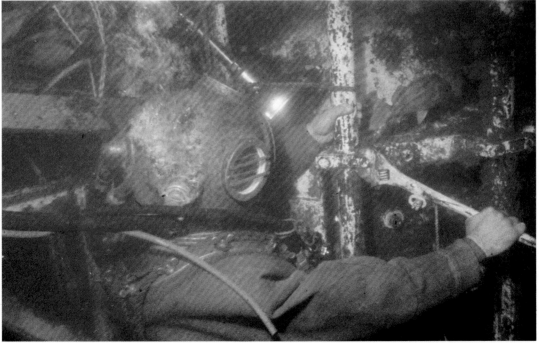

Silhouetted by filtering sunlight, a breath-holding snorkel diver stalks fish near a Mediterranean reef. Carrying no air supply, he can make only shallow, brief excursions with face mask and spear. A helmeted diver, who can stay down for hours, services a gas well 240 feet down off California.

George Bond once told me: "This principle of cold-purification makes good sense. You know, Cousteau experimented with it by freezing out air impurities in Conshelf Three, and eventually it will be used in all undersea habitats."

Around 1831, a Brooklyn machinist named Charles Condert dreamed up a self-contained outfit for himself—and it did work. To store compressed air he employed a six-inch-diameter copper pipe closed at the ends and bent to circle his waist. Air reached his lungs through a tube leading into his closed dress. He often clambered alone into the tricky currents of the East River, and walked about while excess air bubbled from a small hole in the top of his suit. One day a few large bubbles died unnoticed at the surface—the tube had broken and Condert had drowned. Brief notices of his work tantalized readers on both sides of the Atlantic.

As a boy I read and reread *Twenty Thousand Leagues Under the Sea,* a book that made an ingenious diving rig world famous. Jules Verne invented heroes for his submarine *Nautilus,* but not their basic gear. A French mining engineer and a naval officer had developed that five years earlier, in 1865.

Benoît Rouquayrol and Lt. Auguste Denayrouze equipped their helmet-hose suit with a double-chambered air tank. Compressed air pumped from the surface filled the reservoir on the diver's back, and he inhaled through a hose and mouthpiece. With this new gear, he could breathe more comfortably than ever before, for the inventors had equipped their suit with a demand regulator valve, their most important contribution. It fed air as needed from the reservoir, at exactly the right pressure.

Meanwhile, a wiry and prankish Englishman named Henry Fleuss was taking more chances than he knew. In 1868 he patented

Propelled by flippered feet, a free-moving swimmer 90 feet down in the Aegean Sea glides past a Greek hard-hat sponge diver encumbered with air hose, lifeline, and weights.

BOB KENDALL

45

a fully self-contained apparatus that supplied pure compressed oxygen. He would stay down more than an hour, inhaling the same oxygen again and again while a chamber of caustic potash absorbed carbon dioxide from the breath he exhaled. What Fleuss did not know was that below 25 feet or so pure oxygen becomes so toxic it can cause convulsions and death.

Ten years later Paul Bert published a warning about this poisonous effect. "Pressure," Bert explained, "acts on living beings . . . as a chemical agent changing the proportions of oxygen contained in the blood, and causing . . . toxic symptoms when there is too much."

Luckily, Fleuss escaped harm because he dived in shallow water. Equipment like his demanded the utmost caution, but war created a use for it. Frogmen in World War II wore oxygen rebreathers patterned after Fleuss's closed-circuit system. The gear leaves no telltale stream of bubbles, allowing the underwater combatant to move undetected in enemy waters.

Warfare also brought key developments in the submarine. Beginning with a one-man hand-propelled craft in the American

Divers position a cylindrical instrument package—built to help chart the formation and development of waves—at the bottom of Hanalei Bay in Hawaii. Filming motion pictures in the Red Sea, Captain Cousteau (upper right) breathes from the Aqua-Lung that he helped develop. In a weightless environment, divers at right measure underwater work efficiency in a test tank in California.

Revolution, the underwater boat has evolved through the Civil War and two world wars into the nuclear fleets of today. Now a variety of non-military submersibles are playing their part in the struggle of scientists and engineers to win freedom of the depths for mankind.

For the diver, freedom means more time underwater and greater mobility. The breath-holding diver can swim about easily, but only for seconds; the helmet-hose man can stay down for several hours, but only in a restricted area.

I N THE 1920's AND 1930's, French Navy Comdr. Yves Le Prieur devised a system that transformed the diver from a weighted plodder at the bottom into a free swimmer. He supplied a compressed-air tank and hand-operated breathing valve that, combined with rubber foot fins and a light face mask, allowed the underwater man to move almost effortlessly in any direction.

Now one important step remained—the development of a reliable demand regulator valve simpler and more compact than that invented by Rouquayrol and Denayrouze. This would free the diver's hands of the task of valving air from his tank.

At long last, in 1943, the "demand valve" came to perfection and ushered in a new age of underwater exploration. Cousteau, then a lieutenant commander in the French Navy, and a Parisian engineer, Émile Gagnan, completed the device, adapting and testing and revising it, and then testing it again. Their success put safe diving for sport within the reach of virtually everyone.

I first saw their gear, the Aqua-Lung, in the motion picture *Épaves (Sunken Ships)* in 1944. The film showed Cousteau and his underwater companions, Frédéric Dumas and Philippe Tailliez, swimming fishlike among weed-encrusted wrecks with large compressed-air cylinders on their backs. I watched it twice. The experience so fascinated me that I determined to seek out the man behind this marvelous invention.

I met him in London, and wrote an article on his adventures. Though I sent the story to dozens of publications, they showed no interest. Finally, three years later, in 1948, a new magazine, *Science Illustrated*, published it, and soon I was opening a lot of mail requesting information about the Aqua-Lung. The article caught the attention of Lt. Comdr. F. Douglas Fane, USN, head of an underwater demolition team. Doug later acquired one, and work he performed with the new apparatus won him a Navy commendation.

The Aqua-Lung permitted men to move weightlessly in the sea, with a range never possible before. Cousteau sums it up well: "From this day forward we would swim across miles of country no man had known, free and level, with our flesh feeling what the fish scales know."

Perhaps someday men will roam the depths even more freely, with their lungs breathing water as the gills of fishes do.

At Duke University, Dr. Johannes A. Kylstra, who originated the concept, is continuing experiments begun in 1961. He dissolves salts and compressed oxygen in water, and finds that dogs can live in the fluid up to one hour and emerge safely. And he offers the astonishing probability that man may be able to flood his lungs with this oxygenated water and "breathe" it.

Captain Bond believes the concept will work. "This," George says, "would let a diver descend more than two miles, virtually unaffected by pressure, and pop back up without decompression."

No one knows how man will explore the depths in future years. Or what wonders he will find. But whatever his discoveries, they can hardly prove more remarkable than the ingenuity and courage he has already shown in his invasion of the sea. And surely the majesty of the ocean will continue to inspire him as it has through the ages: "this great and wide sea, wherein are things creeping innumerable, both great and small beasts," just as the Psalmist has said.

Man's dream for centuries: Moving almost as easily as a fish, an Italian explorer searches the encrusted hulk of a World War II ship sunk in 100 feet of water in the Tyrrhenian Sea.

3

Revealing the Ocean's Secrets

BY ROBERT C. COWEN

Upending for science, the research craft FLIP, for Floating Instrument Platform, sinks into position off southern California. Developed by the Scripps Institution of Oceanography in nearby La Jolla, FLIP records underwater sounds and measures currents and waves.

AN AIR OF ANTICIPATION stirred our small gathering of science writers at the first of a series of private lectures held during Canada's Expo 67. Beside Professor J. Tuzo Wilson of the University of Toronto, an internationally prominent earth scientist, a pot simmered over a gas flame. I craned my neck for a better view, and caught the aroma of tomato soup!

"The science of the earth," he said, "is in a state of intense excitement." He tipped the pot as he spoke and I saw what I have often observed in my own kitchen — a light froth floating on top of a mass of liquid that roiled and overturned. Soup heated near the bottom of the pot rose to the surface, spread, cooled, and sank again to complete the motion physicists call convection.

"We have been accustomed to regarding the earth as a solid object, like a stone," Dr. Wilson continued. "It is hard to visualize that it may bear much more resemblance to a pot convecting on a stove. Such a pot has a two-phase surface of soup and froth. The floors of the ocean, like the soup, are forever turning over and being renewed while the continents, like the froth, persist and grow."

Older views presented our planet as a rigid, almost static body jiggled occasionally by slight disturbances, holding its oceans in basins of solid rock. Now geophysicists talk of heat flowing from the earth's interior, of ocean floors growing and spreading as molten rock wells up in the rift valleys of the Mid-Oceanic Ridge.

As experts conclude that the bed of the sea is dynamic in nature, they reconsider their concepts of the overlying waters. For oceanography, as Dr. John Lyman put it to me, is "the scientific study of the oceans, their contents and boundaries." Dr. Lyman, special consultant to the Office of Naval Research and the United Nations, speaks from practical experience.

Once when I pressed Dr. Roger Revelle, formerly director of the Scripps Institution of Oceanography at La Jolla, California, to define members of his profession, he smiled wryly and said, "They're sailors who use big words." These specialists include

51

Moored to a breaker-lashed cliff, the British corvette Challenger sends boats along a lifeline to explore St. Paul's Rocks in the mid-Atlantic. Trailblazer in oceanography, the ship sailed from Portsmouth, England, on December 21, 1872, for a voyage that spanned three and a half years and 68,890 nautical miles. Fitted with an auxiliary steam engine in addition to her sails, she carried a crew of about 240 and cruised with 16 of her 18 guns removed to make room for equipment to take soundings and bottom samples. Expedition scientists plumbed the great ocean basins, recorded sea currents and temperatures, and gleaned from the deep 715 new genera and 4,417 species of plants and animals. A twine dredge bag (left), dragged along the ocean floor, netted many of the specimens. Trailing behind the bag, eight hempen tangles swept up bits of coral, sponges, and other organisms.

Chief scientist of the Challenger *expedition,* Scottish naturalist Charles Wyville Thomson headed a six-man ocean-research team. In the *"natural history work-room" (below) on the ship's main deck, the staff examined its findings and preserved samples in test tubes and bottles.*

"THE VOYAGE OF THE CHALLENGER, THE ATLANTIC," VOLUME 1, 1877

geologists, biologists, physicists, chemists, and engineers. Dr. Columbus Iselin of Woods Hole Oceanographic Institution in Massachusetts summed it up for me: "An oceanographer is a research scientist who doesn't get too seasick to do his job."

When H.M.S. *Challenger* sailed from England in 1872, naturalists aboard had to cope with both seasickness and naval etiquette. They returned three and a half years, 68,890 nautical miles later, completing the first great voyage of deep-sea exploration.

Their chief, Charles Wyville Thomson,

THE AUTHOR: *Robert C. Cowen, science editor since 1959 of the* Christian Science Monitor, *received his Master of Science degree in meteorology from the Massachusetts Institute of Technology in 1950. A resident of Concord, Massachusetts, he is the author of* Frontiers of the Sea, *a comprehensive study of the science of oceanography, first published in 1960.*

and other men of science had persuaded the government to sponsor the expedition. The Lords of the Admiralty lent a corvette specially fitted for research.

Oceanographers still enjoy stories of that mission: At first even the cabin boys gathered eagerly when a dredge broke the surface, to watch for rarities or even "living fossils." But as H. N. Moseley, the coral expert, noted, "the same tedious animals kept appearing from the depths," and at last even most of the scientists went on eating when the dredge came up during dinner.

At 362 observing stations, officers and crew helped the six civilians record weather, current speeds, and water temperatures. Wherever they could, they dragged a trawl. Thomson's enthusiasm never flagged; he patiently examined every cuttlefish from every haul. The men spent hours lowering a weighted rope to take soundings, and

their parrot Robert learned to chant, "What! 2,000 fathoms and no bottom!"

Reports of their work fill 50 large and useful illustrated volumes with details on seawater, marine life, and submarine geology. But from isolated soundings with lead and line no one could glimpse the sea floor's true complexity.

Until the echo sounder came into use in the 1920's, oceanographers pictured the land of the abyss as a smooth, monotonous plain, shrouded by sediments that covered any original features. Gradually, a far more dramatic seascape has appeared.

Its mountains include earth's longest range—the last to reach the maps. "Only a decade ago," Dr. Bruce C. Heezen of Columbia University's Lamont Geological Observatory recalls, "I sat down with Maurice Ewing, who led the Mid-Atlantic Ridge Expeditions sponsored by Columbia,

Woods Hole, and the National Geographic Society back in the 1940's. We pored over thousands of world-wide soundings collected by our research schooner, *Vema*. We suspected that the Mid-Atlantic Ridge might link together with other ranges to form a titanic feature, so immense that no one had imagined it."

I wrote enthusiastically about their theories, and got friendly warnings that the "Lamont crowd" was jumping to conclusions. Today that conclusion ranks as one of the major ocean discoveries of our time.

Many scientists think that along this

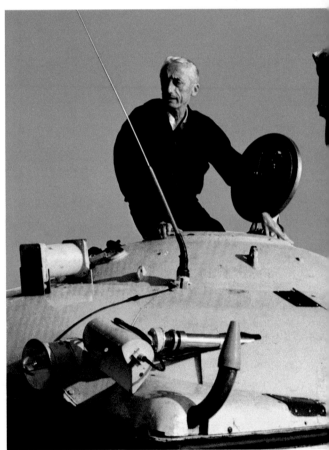

Captain Cousteau emerges from his diving saucer after a cruise hundreds of feet down in the Caribbean. Battery-powered hydrojet nozzles, one on each side, propel the vehicle. The research ship Calypso *(left) serves as floating headquarters for the undersea pioneer's world-wide expeditions. A stern winch holds the saucer.*

Launching a fiberglass "doughnut" 300 miles east of New Jersey, crewmen of the research ship Chain *set up a recording station in the first line of oceanographic buoys ever anchored to monitor the Gulf Stream. The tripod holds an anemom-* *eter and a radio with a homing signal; meters on a mooring line measure deepwater currents. Developed by Dr. William S. Richardson of the Woods Hole Oceanographic Institution in Massachusetts, the 14 buoys went on duty in 1961.*

Brass Nansen bottle will trap a water sample in an Indian Ocean deep, and record its temperature.

Ocean bottom seismograph, its protective steel sphere removed, records signals from undersea detonations.

On a platform of the U. S. Navy's oceanographic research ship Sands, *scientists lower a weighted tube to extract a core sample of sea-floor sediment from the Atlantic. Wearing headphones for intership communication, oceanographer Larry Hawkins (left) watches as an oscilloscope monitors the position of a deep-sea camera.*

ridge system convection currents rise within the earth, driven by heat that builds up as radioactive minerals disintegrate. Moving out from under the ridge, this material tends to pull it apart, splitting open the rift valleys along its crest and causing the sea floor to spread as much as several centimeters a year.

Meanwhile, other sections of the floor may be folding under again in the deep trenches, completing the convection cycle we saw illustrated in the bubbling soup.

This expansion may be pushing the continents apart. In 1912 German meteorologist Alfred Wegener aroused new interest in the notion of drifting continents. Any-

one can see how neatly South America's bulge would snuggle into West Africa's bight, but no one could explain what moved such huge land masses until the concept of the dynamic earth began to take shape. Continental drift remains a controversial theory, but today more geophysicists are accepting it as the evidence piles up.

Oceanographers must gather their data bit by bit, and most of them still work from the deck of a surface ship. Dredges bring up rocks, animals, and plants; fingers of steel plunge into bottom ooze to measure the heat flow from the earth's interior and to punch out long cores of sediment.

Getting cores takes time and patience.

Free of her towline, the 355-foot-long FLIP lies level before flipping. The prow rises and the stern sinks as crewmen flood ballast tanks with 1,500 tons of seawater to submerge 300 feet of her hull in the subsurface calm. When standing on end, the unanchored vessel bobs only inches in

Dr. Lyman remarks: "You spend an hour lowering a 50-foot tube and an hour and a half raising it. Then you push your sample out with a plunger, and often you find you don't have anything but 6 inches of large pebbles that clogged the tube."

Once a scientist gets a good core onto a table, he slices it lengthwise with a knife. I have seen layers of fine-grained sediment reveal colors that rival fine marble: brown silt, red clay, gray ooze, yellow strips of clean sand, green traces of glauconite, and calcareous bands of white. Some measure less than an inch thick, some more than a yard, many between these limits.

Like a long calendar, these layers stretch backward into time and give a glimpse of the ancient world. Settling over the eons, a quiet dustfall of the remains of plants and animals mingles with meteorites and other particles to build up the sea bottom.

Examining pinches of sediment under the microscope, I have seen perfectly preserved shells of tiny sea creatures long extinct—radiolarians as lacy as snowflakes, foraminifers that lived only in cold water and others that flourished in warmer seas.

Paleontologists have identified these animals from their characteristic shapes, and, by distinguishing between species that lived in warm or cool water, they can trace variations of ocean temperatures in the past.

SCRIPPS INSTITUTION OF OCEANOGRAPHY

gale-force winds and seas. Air compressors blow water from the tanks to return the craft to the horizontal. The prow holds laboratories, living quarters, and power units.

Given enough samples for laboratory study, scientists can follow invasions of Arctic waters moving south under the gray skies of the Ice Age, or mild currents running north from the tropics.

"At Lamont," geologist David B. Ericson once told me, "we have one of the world's largest deep-sea core libraries. By comparing strata of sediment, we have traced the advances and retreats of the glaciers for the past one and a half million years."

His colleagues, Dr. Heezen and Dr. Dragoslav Ninkovich, have analyzed two layers of white ash that stripe cores from the bed of the Mediterranean. These and other studies have led Marine Engineer James Watt Mavor, Jr., of Woods Hole Oceanographic Institution, to a prehistoric Minoan city, possibly the site of fabled Atlantis.

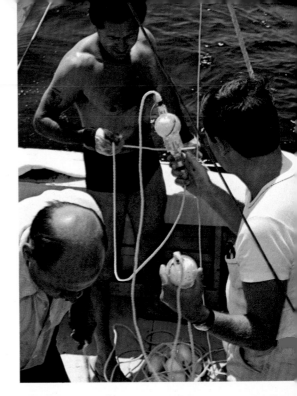

Of all the sea's legends, the tale of Atlantis remains supremely haunting—how a marvelous island commonwealth flourished until the waters engulfed it in a day and a night. Oceanographers found no sign of this "lost continent," but seismologist Anghelos G. Galanopoulos of Athens suggested in 1960 that Atlantis might lie in the Aegean Sea.

There, about 1500 B.C., the island of

Thíra fell apart in a stupendous volcanic eruption. Fields vanished in the steaming waters; huge waves smashed at Crete, 70 miles to the south, where ruins of the great Minoan palaces show the destruction wrought by earthquakes.

After visiting Thíra with the research vessel *Chain*, Mavor organized a Greco-American expedition to study the island. Archeologist Spyridon Marinatos of the University of Athens led the group; Professor Emily Vermeule, of Boston's Museum of Fine Arts, assisted him. In July, 1967, they announced the discovery of a city buried in ash, its houses still intact, with frescoes of marinescapes to display the art of the first high civilization of the West.

While Professor Marinatos continues his work, Mavor studies ash samples from

Aboard Calanus, *research vessel of the University of Miami's Institute of Marine Science, inventor Shale Niskin (in trunks) hauls in recorders that measure ocean-current fields. Below, the instruments record bottom currents in the Straits of Florida. A hard-candy disk links bulb and conical weight. When the candy melts, the pink-topped tubes will pop to the surface.*

JERRY GREENBERG

Thíra to help determine the best way of excavating the city. New clues to the origins of classical Greece may be hidden there, in the realm of the sea-kings of Crete.

Like the archeologist, the oceanographer must often grope for what lies buried. What he cannot see, he has learned to hear, with instruments that interpret for him.

Signals from an electric spark or the rumbling bass from an explosive charge enter the sea bed, where layers of different densities reflect them back to the surface at different time intervals. From the patterns of returning sound waves, geologists analyze the land far beneath their ship.

The pace of research has quickened since high-pitched sound pulses replaced the miles of rope and wire — unwieldy and subject to breaking — that early oceanographers payed out to measure the depths. Now the "ping" from an echo sounder bounces off the bottom and the instrument automatically calculates depth from the elapsed time between sending and receiving. A recorder on deck logs a continuous profile.

Thanks to the speed of the echo sounder, many of the larger features of the sea floor have been mapped. Yet reefs still claim unwary ships, and oceanographers expect to meet the unknown, just as in the days of *Challenger*'s lonely voyage.

Samuel W. Matthews of the NATIONAL GEOGRAPHIC recalled one such encounter from his travels of some 40,000 miles with the International Indian Ocean Expedition.

"Seven hundred nautical miles out from

INSTITUTE OF MARINE SCIENCE, UNIVERSITY OF MIAMI

South Africa and 450 south of Madagascar, S.A.S. *Natal* chanced one night on a shoal where no shoal should be. Her depth recorder showed the bottom rising suddenly to a jagged reef scarcely 60 feet down. *Natal* had found the uncharted peak of a huge, steep-sided seamount, towering some 16,000 feet above true oceanic depths."

When Sam talks about the IIOE, he leaves no doubt about how far oceanography has come in the past century. "Until recently," he says, "the Indian Ocean was pretty much a mystery. But in 1959 some 30 nations set out to take its measure, with 40 ships that logged a million miles across that windswept expanse. Out of more than six years' work, we have the portrait of an ocean—currents, mountains, plants, animals. It will take years to analyze all the information, but a task of unprecedented scope lies in the wake of those 40 ships."

A greater task remains. Dr. Lyman says: "At the present rate of survey work, it might take 40 years to get an adequate mapping of the ocean floor."

Struggling against the overpowering immensity of their subject, the scientists who study the circulation of the ocean waters find clues in the waves. Stirred by the winds and by the tide-ruling forces of the sun and moon, the sea presents a kaleidoscopic panorama, sometimes regular, sometimes chaotic, whose rhythms often signal a meaning.

Booming breakers on our western shores hint of typhoons that raged thousands of miles away. Choppy whitecaps in a channel may tell of ebb tide flowing against opposing winds or swell. Incoming waves along a beach may reflect the contour of the offshore bottom—they rise higher over banks and sandbars, or break with lower crests after crossing a submarine canyon.

Opening like a book, a water sampler helps contribute a chapter to man's knowledge of the sea. Triggered at a predetermined depth, the metal covers pop open and a sterile plastic bag traps water, then seals automatically. In the Straits of Florida, a marine biologist winches the apparatus aboard Calanus *(right). At the Institute of Marine Science, research aide Rose Cefalu studies microbe cultures produced from water samples brought up from varying depths.*

Everywhere, sun and moon pull the sea into motion, but the shape of basins and shores determines the local timing and range of the tides. For instance, in the Gulf of Mexico the tide rises and falls once a day, and only by a foot or two; at Río Gallegos, Argentina, it changes twice a day, with a range of 45 feet, 7 inches.

Quite apart from tides, however, the interlocking water masses of the oceans are forever on the move. Sometimes they rush along with stupefying power, as when the Gulf Stream pours past Miami and surges up the coast. Sometimes they barely creep, like the cold bottom currents that may take decades to complete their journey. But somehow every drop of water will find its way to almost every part of the sea's domain.

This movement of the waters stirs the

oceans continually. It regulates the weather. It creates upwelling currents that bring nitrates, phosphates, and other minerals from the depths, fertilizing the plants that feed the world's great fisheries.

"To build a comprehensive science of the sea, we must first understand its basic circulation"—all oceanographers say this. For centuries shipmasters have logged currents, yet scientists have scarcely begun to sort out all the data on hand.

Aboard the U. S. Coast and Geodetic Survey's new ship, *Discoverer,* I saw both new and old methods used. I inspected new deep-current meters as well as devices that measure surface currents, water temperature, and salinity. Then I watched a technician take a wire and lower a dozen of the old Nansen bottles to collect water samples. When they reached their intended depths, a weight slid after them, triggering a mechanism that tipped them over to get their samples. Thermometers on the bottles recorded the temperatures.

As they came up again, the technician turned to me. "The new direct-reading gadgets are useful," he said, "but we still have to bring the water aboard like this for real precision." He took his samples to a lab to check their chemical properties, including oxygen content and salinity. The ratio of salts to water varies, and he had an instrument to measure it electrically.

"With enough samples like these and a lot of math," Dr. Lyman remarks, "we can plot the currents—they may be elusive, but they're not whimsical. The rotation of the earth, the winds, and the density of the water control their flow. Density, of course, depends on salinity and temperature."

Adding two tablespoons of salt to a quart of fresh water gives the average "saltiness" of the open oceans; but rain and rivers dilute many seas, and evaporation makes areas like the Red and Sargasso Seas more saline. As water gets saltier, it grows denser, or heavier.

Salinity varies slightly in the oceans; temperature causes even greater differences in density because it varies far more — from the freezing point, 29° F., near the poles, to 85° in the Red Sea, with an average of 65° in the Northern Hemisphere and 61° in the Southern. Frigid levels of Arctic and Antarctic water inch along the sea floor. Oceanographers draw their maps on the basis of these facts, and consider them woefully inadequate, for most of these charts represent averages only.

The Gulf Stream, giant river of the sea, remains mysterious in spite of long and determined assaults upon it. In 1958 Henry Stommel, a specialist in ocean circulation, described to me a radical and complex theory based on his concept that differences in water density and not wind cause current movement in the depths. In 1957 he had announced that this theory would explain a strong southward-flowing countercurrent under the Gulf Stream.

At Woods Hole, Dr. Alan J. Faller tested Stommel's calculations with large, round, water-filled tanks spinning to duplicate the earth's rotation. Wooden segments inside represented continental land masses.

"This particular model shows only the bottom mile of the North Atlantic," he told me. "We slowly add water dyed blue to the northern part, to represent cold water sinking from the surface. Now — you can see the Gulf Stream countercurrent." I watched the blue dye flow "south along the coastline" just as Stommel had predicted it would. Within two years, the ocean itself

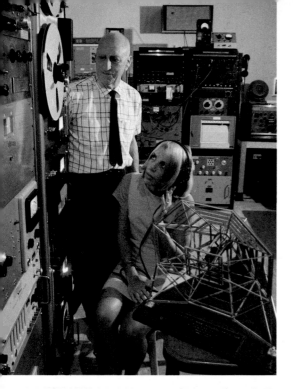

dramatically confirmed such experiments.

"We can set this float to remain within a hundred meters of any depth we choose," explained Dr. John C. Swallow when he showed me a ten-foot aluminum tube he had developed. "It sends out an identifying ping." He used it to check Stommel's idea. Dropping these "pingers" into deep water off South Carolina, he tracked them from the surface. At depths between 8,400 and 9,600 feet, seven pingers moved south. Stommel's Gulf Stream countercurrent passed from theory into fact.

Experiments like this require many instruments and much money, and current specialists fume at a lack of both. While all oceanographers wait for more data on the currents, marine biologists have plenty of materials to work with as they keep chipping away at the enigma of life.

"Water is the pre-eminent substance of our kind of life," says Roger Revelle. "We now believe the ocean was the womb which

Sounds of the sea intrigue a data analyst as Dr. John C. Steinberg plays a recording from an underwater acoustic projector (below). A model of the transmitter rests near them, in the Acoustic Laboratory of the Institute of Marine Science.

first nourished and protected Earth's children." And they, of course, occur nowhere in such giddy profusion as in the sea. Countless billions of microscopic plants stand at the very beginning of the ocean's long food chain, for they feed equally countless billions of microscopic animals. Together, these tiny creatures make up a teeming community known as plankton.

SIR ALISTER HARDY of Oxford University, an outstanding authority on marine life, feels that "in the plankton we may find an assemblage of animals more diverse and more comprehensive than is to be seen in any other realm of life."

One day at Oxford, Sir Alister slid a plankton sample under a microscope for me. Diatoms, one of the most numerous of the plankton, glistened from their transparent silica shells like gems in little crystal caskets. Some, joined in long chains, shone like diamond bracelets. The diatoms share the ocean meadows with a second large group of plants, called flagellates. With their whiplike flagella, they keep themselves from sinking out of the sunlit upper water, where they live by photosynthesis.

Investigators of this living broth have detected some astonishing patterns of behavior. As light waxes and wanes, animals of the plankton carry out a curious vertical migration. At night they climb toward the darkened surface, only to sink again with the rising of the sun. Some species regularly travel several thousand feet, a considerable effort for such weak swimmers.

For about 25 years scientists have been striving to fit one of the more mysterious pieces of this biological puzzle into place— the so-called Deep Scattering Layers that echo sounders sometimes record as a "phantom bottom." Found in every ocean, the DSL's rise by night and sink by day, suggesting that, whatever they are, they live.

"One of the really important things in ocean science today," Dr. Lyman said not long ago, "is the discovery that some of the creatures of the DSL's produce carbon monoxide. They're siphonophores, kin to jellyfish and Portuguese men-of-war."

I asked how this discovery came about.

"Well, Dr. Eric Barham at the Naval Electronics Laboratory Center in San Diego went down in the bathyscaph *Trieste* and looked at the components of the DSL's. Until very recently, we thought they had to be fish. Their swim bladders, with gas inside, would give the kind of echo usually received on the sounders. But Barham noticed these siphonophores, *Nanomia bijuga*.

"They're spectacular—six inches to two feet long: a crimson-capped blob with delicate translucent white tendrils trailing along behind—beautiful agile things.

"When Barham sampled them, he found that the float—that's the blob—contains gas bubbles, 80 percent carbon monoxide. When the beasties rise to the surface at night the gas jets off into the water. Just how they tolerate such high concentrations is perplexing, because carbon monoxide is an excellent poison.

"Let's speculate a little. Say you want to start a fish farm. Maybe your first step should be to eliminate siphonophores—in effect, to keep the wolves out of your pasture. But you wouldn't want to do that until you're certain just how this affects the whole biological setup, and we don't know that yet. We have a long way to go."

The sea-going scientists carry on their work, and it yields all sorts of practical benefits. For example, seismograph systems now guard Pacific coasts and islands, warning them when to expect dangerous tsunamis, the misnamed "tidal waves" set off by undersea earthquakes.

But the value of marine research defies prediction: Chemicals from shellfish and sponges may yield new wonder drugs to control pain or virus infections. Here study has just begun. Thus, as oceanographers extend their knowledge, they bring unexpected gifts into our lives.

Underwater TV camera sends sights and sounds of sea life to monitors a mile away on Bimini Island. The unit, controlled from shore, can rotate 360° and tilt up and down. A once-a-month scrubbing removes algae from its plexiglass dome.

4

Diving for Sport and for Science

BY BILL BARADA

Roaming a coral reef off Hawaii, amateur divers hunt marine life with cameras and spearguns. Such part-time adventurers have assisted scientists by inventing, testing, and developing underwater equipment.

SLIPPING INTO THE WATERS of the Pacific at Rangiroa Atoll, I flippered my way into the larger of two submarine passes that split the reef. Cautiously, I began to creep down one of its coral walls. Beside me, my friends Al Giddings and Dewey Bergman moved with the same discretion. The reasons for our vigilance were all around us—throngs of foraging sharks, including grays, black tips, and white tips.

We had planned this hazardous undersea itinerary with the hope of making a film documentary on sharks in a "feeding frenzy." Like many divers before us, we sought to pierce some of the riddles of shark behavior by observing and recording it at close quarters. We had found a perfect "studio" here in the Tuamotu Archipelago. In this cleft in the coral, hundreds of five- to ten-foot sharks prowl a 300-yard-wide, mile-long strip of water.

As the darkly ominous shapes swarmed about us, Dewey and Al got set with their movie cameras. I had a still camera, but my main job was to shoot fish with my speargun, attracting sharks to the bait and sending them into action.

The sharks began swimming quietly on all sides of us, keeping a distance of about 15 feet—too far for good filming. Each time I aimed the speargun, one shark would line up behind my target. I could see his eyes rolling as he waited for me to fire. Excited, the others moved swiftly around him. When a 15-pound snapper swam into range between the cameras, I shot it. The sharks went wild, coming at us from all directions as they raced for the fish.

Dodging the voracious predators, Al and Dewey swept their cameras over the mad scene while I gripped the harpoon line with one hand and held myself fast to the coral with the other. When a shark hit the fish on the end of the line and took off, a pack of about 50 zoomed into a tight circle over our heads. The piece of coral I clung to snapped off, and the thrashing brutes fighting over the fish on the end of the line began pulling me toward them. I let go of the line and watched gratefully as the battling pack swam away with the prize.

Five days and 2,500 feet of film later, we concluded our dives among these dreaded creatures. We had found that sharks don't always live up to their reputation of being dangerous man-eaters—at least not until familiarity really starts breeding contempt. Each day they became more aggressive, and we had a number of very close brushes.

Why did they tolerate us at all? Was it the fresh seafood dinners we provided? Perhaps. As investigators know so well, sharks react unpredictably to the presence of human beings, but most often attack surface swimmers or those who have been injured or appear distressed. Our self-contained underwater breathing apparatus, or scuba, let us move about among them with ease and control.

Marine biologists who have seen the film tell us it represents an important addition to the archives on shark behavior. If so, it

THE AUTHOR: *Bill Barada, marketing manager for* Skin Diver *magazine and developer of several items of underwater equipment, began diving in 1935 when the sport was called "goggle fishing." In 1940 he formed the Los Angeles Neptunes, one of the first diving clubs in the U.S. He is the author of four books on diving and several scripts for the* Sea Hunt *TV series.*

will be only one of countless contributions made by amateur divers to the fund of knowledge about the sea and its denizens.

David R. Stith, president of the Underwater Society of America, agrees with me that sports divers are playing a far bigger role in underwater developments than anyone anticipated. As Dave put it: "They have come up with a lot of invaluable information, techniques, and improved equipment. And if the confident amateur hadn't led the way, many of the marine scientists and engineers who are now getting wet might have taken much longer to use scuba as the vital research tool it is."

The art of diving had progressed unbelievably between my shark dive in 1966 and the day in 1935 when, with only a homemade spear and goggles, I first peered into the undersea world off Palos Verdes Peninsula, California. I had been spurred to this adventure by hearing that the world's first skin-diving club, the Bottom Scratchers of San Diego, had formed in 1933. And Guy Gilpatric had inflamed my imagination with descriptions of spearfishing in the Mediterranean in a magazine article, "The Compleat Goggler," which later became the title of his famous book. But nothing

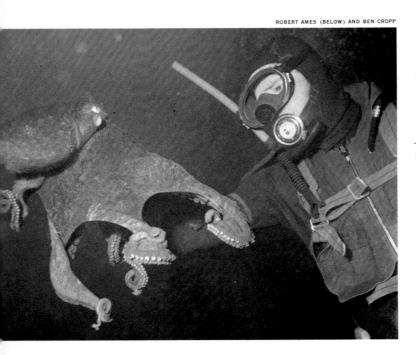

Clutching a 12-foot tiger shark killed 40 feet down on Australia's Great Barrier Reef, a spearfisherman struggles toward the surface with his catch. Tigers prowl both near the shore and in the open sea, eating everything from sea gulls to fellow sharks. Divers regard this predator as one of the sea's most dangerous creatures.

Writhing octopus strains to pull free of a diver intruding upon its domain in 60 feet of water off California. The naturally timid animal, once considered a deadly menace to swimmers, usually retreats or camouflages itself when man approaches.

Census takers with plastic slates and grease pencils count Florida Keys reef fishes for the American Littoral Society, an aquatic study and conservation group. A Sandy Hook Marine Laboratory diver collects swaying current detectors off New Jersey, and an amateur diver with a slurp gun captures wrasses for his home aquarium by drawing them into a water-filled chamber.

had prepared me for the reality of my first goggle dive. Mesmerized, I floated above a breathtaking seascape of color and movement. A jungle of kelp and seaweed undulated with the swells. Jagged rocks bristled with dazzling arrays of clinging organisms. Weaving through kelp and peeking out from holes in the rocks, garibaldi goldfish, perch, and rockfish kept a wary eye on me.

Several times I dived to about 20 feet and learned the limitations of my crude equipment. The goggles pressed tightly against my eyes, the spear impeded my progress, and almost as soon as I touched bottom my lungs ached for want of air and I hastened

back to the surface. Within 15 minutes I "froze out" from the chill of the water and returned to shore. But I firmly resolved to continue exploring this enchanting world.

My diving friends and I faced the constant frustration of inadequate equipment. At first, we improvised goggles. Later, we chanced upon some face masks imported from Japan. These suggested ways of making our own, and we greatly improved our range of vision as well as our enjoyment of the beauty below.

In 1940, Olympic yachtsman Owen P. Churchill, of Los Angeles, introduced rubber swim fins into the United States. He

told me that he had seen divers in Tahiti wearing them. When he found they had been developed by French Navy Comdr. Louis de Corlieu, he bought the patent rights for the United States market. These flippers increased our speed and range. By taking the work out of swimming, the fins allowed amateurs to dive like experts.

Then veterans of World War II under-water demolition teams brought home their rubber frogman suits. A member of my club, the Los Angeles Neptunes, obtained one, and fellow divers immediately began making copies, cementing them together in garage workshops. Protecting us from the cold and keeping us dry, the suits increased our endurance time, and we could enjoy hours of diving in comfort.

WILLIAM STEPHENS

Speargun poised, ichthyologist Eugenie Clark searches for reef fish among sponges and sea fans near Grand Cayman Island in the Caribbean. Like many marine biologists, she began diving to survey the underwater world firsthand.

up under colorful names—the Boston Sea Rovers, Coast of Maine Neptunes, and the Puget Sound Mudsharks. This mask-and-fin, hold-your-breath period saw divers taking great pride in exhibiting their prowess, stamina, and courage. Spearfishing gave ample opportunity for such expression, and competitive meets became the vogue.

For some time we had been using the snorkel, a tube permitting us to breathe while facedown on the surface. But every diver dreamed of obtaining a simple, safe device for breathing underwater. The oxygen breathing gear used by Navy frogmen did not qualify for amateurs. It could bring disaster to the uninformed, because pure oxygen becomes a deadly poison if divers go too deep.

The dream began to materialize in 1949 when a California sporting-goods dealer imported the Aqua-Lung. Interest should have exploded like a bomb, but it didn't. For one thing, a basic set of scuba, including a half-hour tank of air, cost $250, several times today's price. Most dealers knew nothing about diving and less about the Aqua-Lung, since the first directions for its use were in French. And for a time no air stations existed to recharge the tanks.

I acquired my first Aqua-Lung in 1950 by trading the importer three rubber suits I had developed. He gave me oversimplified instructions, to say the least: "You know how to dive. Just put on your 'lung' and go ahead. It's automatic." I loaded my new equipment into a rubber boat and, with my wife Harriet, headed for the kelp beds off Point Dume, near Malibu.

The use of quick-release buckles and slip hitches that allow instant removal of a tank —a basic safety rule of present-day scuba instruction—was unknown then. I tightly strapped on my tank so it couldn't possibly work loose, then slipped into the water.

Now divers can choose between ready-made "dry" suits and "wet" suits, the latter first developed and manufactured by an amateur. Air trapped inside the cellular foam rubber or neoprene of a wet suit provides insulation. Water seeping under the suit is kept warm by body heat.

When diving suits broke the cold-water barrier in the late 1940's, new clubs sprang

Captive killer whale, Namu permits inspection of his formidable array of teeth by Edward I. Griffin, director of the Seattle Public Aquarium. The 24-foot relative of the porpoise, seeking food and companionship, glides under Griffin's skiff and overturns it, spilling his keeper and a load of salmon. Namu's playfulness contradicts the belief that these whales are invariably killers.

PAUL V. THOMAS

Five-ton Namu cavorts in Rich Cove near Seattle after eating part of his daily ration of 400 pounds of salmon, costing $100. Owner Griffin towed his Orcinus orca *in an underwater pen from British Columbia, where a fishing net accidentally snared the whale. Scientists listened to Namu's heartbeat and recorded his language of sonarlike beeps and squeals.*

MERRILL P. SPENCER

Straddling Namu's broad back for a 15-minute romp, Griffin clutches the high dorsal fin for balance. "So sensitive is the fin," says Griffin, "that at first the touch of a finger alarmed Namu, and he would quickly shake me off." The bull whale soon became so accustomed to his companion that at times he slept with him aboard.

It took only a few minutes to adjust to the Aqua-Lung before I felt an exhilarating sense of freedom. I breathed as naturally underwater as on the surface! Moving like a fish, I swam through stands of giant kelp, hovered above a rocky pinnacle, and lingered along the face of a cliff. I drifted down, gliding into depths I had never reached before and quickly found an abundance of abalone, lobsters, and fish to fill the sack I carried. All too soon my air gave out and I started to ascend.

On the surface I ran into trouble. I came up in the midst of a heavy kelp bed, 50 yards from the boat. Water that had leaked into my suit and 16 pounds of lead in my belt weighted me down. Although accustomed to holding my breath and swimming beneath the kelp canopy, I had never reckoned with an air tank in this circumstance. My tank, fouled in the kelp and partly out of water, became heavier, pushing me under. Gasping for air and struggling to stay afloat, I fumbled desperately with the straps of the Aqua-Lung and the weight belt. If Harriet had not reached me in time with the boat, it could have been my last dive.

When Captain Cousteau's remarkable book of diving adventures, *The Silent World*, appeared in 1953, Aqua-Lung sales began to go up in the United States. The boom continued as the public watched underwater motion pictures and television shows. But knowledge about Aqua-Lungs failed to increase at an equal pace, and untrained divers sometimes met with disaster.

A typical example of the attitude that

THOMAS NEBBIA

prevailed occurred during a club dive off Santa Catalina Island. Three strangers, each with a full set of new equipment, joined us aboard a chartered boat. I discovered none had ever dived before. When I suggested they practice with mask, fins, and snorkel before putting on their tanks, one said, "We can't do that. We have to be able to breathe because none of us can swim." After I told them the facts of scuba diving they decided to stay on the boat.

Anticipating the threat of restrictive legislation and anxious to avoid it by establishing their own controls, diving clubs began forming into regional councils. In 1959 the councils joined together as the Underwater Society of America. The society in turn became the largest constituency of the World Underwater Federation, established in Paris later that same year.

When *Skin Diver* magazine first appeared in 1951, its pages informed divers of problems besetting their sport and offered suggestions for finding solutions. The search for means to ensure safety began in earnest on the west coast.

Bevly B. Morgan, then a lifeguard with the Los Angeles County Department of Parks and Recreation, became concerned over the growing number of rescues involving scuba divers. He advised county officials to enlist the services of experts in setting up classes on diving safety.

The expert divers who were invited included two graduate students at the Scripps Institution of Oceanography—the late Conrad Limbaugh and Andreas B. Rechnitzer. Both went on to win recognition as marine scientists. Their group produced the first book of safety rules for divers and launched a program to certify instructors.

By 1966, the Los Angeles County program had certified 360 instructors who had trained 97,000 skin divers and scuba divers. Meanwhile, clubs around the country began to employ this successful system.

Branches of the YMCA welcomed diving clubs and started a project for certifying

DRAWING BY NATIONAL GEOGRAPHIC ARTIST ROBERT W. NICHOLSON

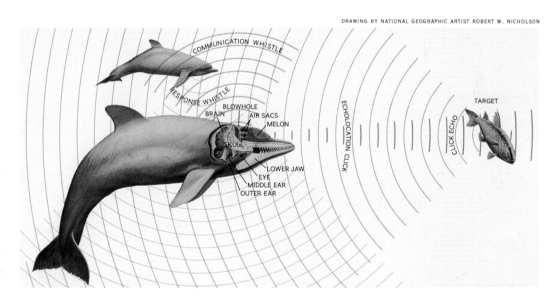

Porpoises rocket 12 feet high in response to an underwater electronic command at Sea Life Park near Honolulu. The versatile mammal, with a brain larger and possibly more complex than man's, helps in undersea work by carrying messages and guiding divers to lost companions. The porpoise, or dolphin, uses a form of sonar (above) to obtain an acoustical picture of his surroundings. Scientists believe the animal sends out clicking sounds by forcing air from two sacs near the blowhole. From echoes, he judges the direction, distance, size, and nature of objects around him. To communicate with other porpoises, he "whistles," then listens for the reply.

Natural friends of man, porpoises tow a companion through Sea Life Park's man-made lagoon. Above, frisking mammals obey a command to stay near the boat, beeped to them by a battery-powered signaler. Scientists (below) record the heartbeat and muscular activity of an anesthetized research animal in a Miami laboratory.

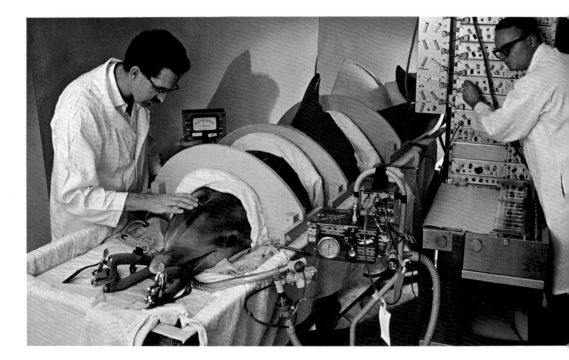

instructors on a national scale. To ensure uniform certification requirements, the National Association of Underwater Instructors was established.

Around the globe, diving enthusiasts took similar steps in the interest of safety. More diving magazines appeared, all providing important educational services for their readers. Through *Triton*, its official magazine, the British Sub-Aqua Club publicized its instruction course, one of the finest in the world.

In 1966 a member of the British House of Lords suggested the need to issue licenses of competency to divers, similar to those required for automobile drivers. The Parliamentary Under-Secretary, Lord Winterbottom, said: "No, my Lords, there is already a marked degree of control exercised by the British Sub-Aqua Club, which controls a large majority of sporting divers in this country. The Club has produced a manual on safe diving which is recognized by the Royal Navy and acknowledged and used throughout the world."

Today, because of the efforts of a few dedicated groups, the sport of diving enjoys an enviable safety record. Accidents rarely occur.

Dave Stith points out that the divers most apt to have accidents are "those with little or no training, or those who are so proficient they start ignoring the fundamentals." Dave adds, "We're finding that trained, attentive divers don't get into any more trouble than fellows who play golf."

In the early days, spearfishing attracted most scuba divers. But as the novelty wore off many of them started looking for underwater activities with a purpose. As a consequence, marine archeology, salvage operations, photography, engineering, and

biology owe a great deal to amateur divers.

For example, along the Pacific coast from San Francisco to Mexico, divers have found thousands of artifacts left behind by prehistoric seashore inhabitants. Just off the La Jolla Beach and Tennis Club, divers have picked up hundreds of mortars and other stone objects, proving the existence of villages beyond the present shoreline as long ago as 3,000 to 7,000 years.

On the east coast the divers' search for useful activities has had significant results. One day in 1960 in the office of Dr. Lionel A. Walford, director of Sandy Hook Marine Laboratory in New Jersey, "a group of divers appeared and demanded something to do."

He put them to work on a number of projects. "From this nucleus of enthusiastic volunteers came the American Littoral Society, organized in 1961," Dr. Walford said. "As amateur naturalists they have accumulated much new information about fish. Of course, they've needed guidance and training, and we're happy to give it to them when time permits."

Now, six years later, the society has about 2,200 members, representing every state. The 700 active divers among them count and tag fish, observe other underwater life, and send reports to the society.

John R. Clark, a member of the laboratory staff and president of the society, said, "Every year a group of Arizona divers goes faithfully to the Gulf of California and makes a fish count, similar to the Audubon Society Christmas bird count. If the group continues monitoring year after year, its reports could reveal a conservation or a pollution problem in time to remedy it before serious damage is done."

According to society member David K. Bulloch of Hillsdale, New Jersey, "Watching undersea creatures gets under your skin. Curiosity brings you back to the same spot week after week to see what has happened to the inhabitants."

He should know. A research chemist, Dave devoted his spare time to observing invertebrates living on a wreck 82 feet down in the Atlantic off Shark River Inlet,

Wearing self-contained underwater breathing apparatus, or scuba, a diver hitches a ride on a loggerhead turtle off the Florida Keys. The huge reptile, its jaws powerful enough to mangle an arm, tries to lose his passenger by plunging to the bottom. In darkness (lower right), the Gorgon's head, or basket star, an animal that resembles a plant, stretches ghostly arms to trap plankton. Crumpling into a matted heap (upper right), the eerie creature assumes its daytime posture.

*Emerging from Florida waters, marine biologist
Walter A. Starck II hands his wife Jo a camera
that he adapted for his ecological studies of Alligator Reef. The Fisheye lens allows a wide field
of view with only slight distortion. At right, it
frames Mrs. Starck among large clumps of brain
and star corals off Lower Matecumbe Key.*

New Jersey. His report in *Underwater Naturalist,* the society's quarterly, brought high
praise from biologists.

In the early 1950's, Conrad Limbaugh
sounded the first call for scientists to use
scuba in studying the marine environment.
Soon afterward, David M. Owen promoted
the same idea at Woods Hole Oceanographic Institution. Today, hundreds of scientists
go down into the ocean to observe and collect, employing equipment and techniques
developed by amateur divers.

In 1959 three of California's original
group of diving scientists, Limbaugh,
Dr. Wheeler J. North, and James R. Stewart,
swimming into a sea canyon during a storm,
became the first to report one of nature's
unsuspected underwater tricks. At Cabo
San Lucas, Baja California, they found

sand falls, which resemble waterfalls with the materials switched around—land plummets through water rather than water through land.

At thirty feet, the divers noticed sand sliding gently down the canyon slope. Following the flow, they swam above a dozen or more falls tumbling among the rocks. Finally, when they reached 130 feet, they saw a spectacular stream of white sand cascading over a sharp dropoff. The storm waves on the surface were cutting sand from the beach and driving it into the canyon. In later descents, Dr. Robert F. Dill swam along sand falls and rapids at 250 feet. From that level he could see the sand river flowing a hundred feet farther down.

Dr. Eugenie Clark, of the Cape Haze Marine Laboratory in Florida, can be found underwater as often as on land, collecting specimens in jars and nets. While diving near Eilat, Israel, she discovered a new species of *Trichonotus*, a small, elongated fish commonly known as a sand diver. Following scientific custom and a mother's prerogative, she named the fish *Trichonotus nikii*, in honor of her son Niki.

Between 1963 and 1966, marine biologist Carleton Ray and his associates braved frigid waters to observe great Weddell seals under the Antarctic ice. "We would be going down with standard breathing equipment," Dr. Ray reported in the NATIONAL GEOGRAPHIC, "but our suits had been specially fabricated for us of 5/16-inch-thick foam neoprene." The only exposed skin was a little area around the mouth, which the men knew from experience would not get uncomfortably cold in icy water.

On one of their first Antarctic dives in 1963, Dr. Ray and Navy Lt. David Lavallee encountered a nine-foot, 800-pound seal heading for the same hole in the ice that was their objective. "Almost together the seal and I popped our heads through the access hole," Dr. Ray said. "On an impulse, I gave him a gentle pat on the snout, and then heaved myself out of the water.

"Dave and I watched the animal breathe deeply and repeatedly for three minutes, his nostrils dilating and contracting like giant mechanical valves. Before he clamped

his nostrils shut and dived again, he gave us one brief glance and that was all.

"I couldn't have been more delighted by his casual acceptance of us. . . . To him we were fellow marine creatures, and he was proving our motto: 'If you want to study a seal, *be* a seal.'"

Under these intimate circumstances, Dr. Ray and his colleagues watched seals beneath the ice snoozing while holding their

breath and also listened to seal "talk." "There was not a moment's silence in the 'silent world,'" Dr. Ray wrote, "but instead a never-ending chorus of seal trills, chirps, and whistles."

Dr. Walter A. Starck II, another diving marine biologist, started using an Aqua-Lung at 14 and soon began taking pictures with a camera in an improvised rubber-bag housing. These beginnings eventually led him to embark on one of the most far-reaching studies of coral-reef life ever made.

About 1958 Walt selected Alligator Reef off the Florida Keys for intensive research. "The Florida coral reefs were about as well studied as any in the world at the time my wife Jo and I started diving there," he told

Amid gnarled antler coral jutting from the sea floor, a swimmer ranges the underwater trail in Buck Island Reef National Monument, U. S. Virgin Islands. In Florida's John Pennekamp Coral Reef Park, the nine-foot bronze statue "Christ of the Deep" stands in 24 feet of water.

ELGIN CIAMPI (BELOW) AND JERRY GREENBERG

me. "But nobody had ever really gone down into the water to see what went on. Scuba let us do just that."

With support from the National Geographic Society and the National Science Foundation, Walt and Jo found 517 species of fish on Alligator Reef—the richest known fish fauna of any area in the New World. "Forty-five of those species were previously unknown in United States waters," he said, "and 18 were completely unknown to science. Gives you an idea of how much we really knew about the reefs before, doesn't it?"

Increasing threats to marine life in coral reefs from pollution, careless spearfishing, and thoughtless coral collectors have prompted conservationists around the world to begin staking off preserves similar to those protecting game and plants in the great national parks. The underwater preserves offer opportunities for both recreation and scientific study.

The first, and one of the most beautiful —John Pennekamp Coral Reef State Park in the Key Largo reefs of Florida—came into being in 1960. Here snorkelers and scuba divers may explore a 21-mile-long submarine coral garden. Protected from shell collectors and spearfishermen, sea life abounds. The fish, like animals in the parks, show no fear of man. Swimming around a diver's head, they peer boldly into his face mask, begging for handouts.

The Japanese Nature Conservation Society is investigating a number of sites for possible use as marine preserves. In France, the famous diver and underwater archeologist, Philippe Tailliez, has played a leading role in establishing the Port Cros Submarine Park near Toulon.

Perhaps the most popular spot for underwater sightseeing, the U. S. Virgin Islands now teem with visitors rambling over and among the coral reefs. The Department of the Interior maintains trails in marine parks off Buck Island and off St. John.

Snorkelers, swimming at the surface, look down at submerged markers 10 to 20 feet below that identify the various types of coral and explain their formation. Some signs show pictures of fish, give their names, and inform the waterborne sightseer about their habits. Even nonswimmers with snorkels can glide above the coral, holding on to floats towed by small craft.

Today the camera replaces the speargun as members of the "wet jet set" use the oceans as their playground. In just 17 years since my first experience with an Aqua-Lung, diving has become as commonplace as skiing.

Occasionally, I feel a touch of nostalgia for those early days when a handful of adventurers probed the mysterious submerged world. More often, though, I remember with pride that the adventurous sports diver prepared the way for an even more exciting era of scientific discovery.

JERRY GREENBERG (BELOW) AND ELGIN CIAMPI

Sails furled, boats hover above their shadows in Buck Island's turquoise-green lagoon. Sloops and catamarans ferry snorkel swimmers and scuba divers to the barrier reef from nearby St. Croix. In Pennekamp Park, an underwater visitor offers a bit of sea urchin to a venturous white grunt. Tiny bluehead wrasses wait for leftovers.

5

Cameras Below

BY LUIS MARDEN

Amphibious marine iguana, found only in the Galapagos Islands, grazes on brown algae as sea chubs float above. Underwater photography reveals dimensions of the sea long hidden from man.

SHORTLY before the United States entered World War II, I went to the Antilles to write an article for the NATIONAL GEOGRAPHIC on U. S. military bases in the islands. Between bomber flights I stayed for some days on Antigua, and there I had my first look at a coral reef through a diving mask borrowed from a Marine Corps officer.

Like almost everyone else who has known the experience, I was entranced. The eerie beauty and strangeness, the other-worldly landscape and alien life forms, seemed to belong to another planet. Making pictures is part of my profession, and I yearned to photograph the scene. Unhappily, on an island in wartime, I had no way of improvising an underwater camera. So I simply observed and marveled as I explored this mysterious liquid world.

I did not know it at the time, but half a century before, a Frenchman, Louis Boutan, had anticipated my experience.

". . . with regard to the sea," he wrote in a book on underwater photography, "the naturalist is like an inhabitant of the moon sailing through ethereal space, who cannot descend through the atmosphere that surrounds the earth.

"If he wishes to obtain some notion . . . of the globe and its inhabitants, he would have to . . . construct dredges . . . to make contact with the surface of the earth.

"His nets might capture some birds, which would represent for him the most numerous inhabitants of the earth, and, if his dredge were to knock off the top of some factory chimney, he would conclude that it was the mysterious abode of some unknown animal.

"Up to the present, naturalists have operated exactly in this manner in their study of the ocean deeps . . . blindly.

"How the situation would change the moment it becomes possible to take photographs on the bottom of the sea!"

Boutan wrote this in 1900, after he had worked on the problem of the submersible camera for eight years. Almost singlehandedly, he created the art of making pictures underwater. A marine biologist of robust build and questing mind, he made his first descent in helmet and diving dress in July, 1892, in the Mediterranean.

He recalled: "The strangeness of the submarine landscape made a strong impression on me.... I then resolved to try photography. If one can photograph a landscape in open air, why, I asked myself, should it not be possible to make a photograph on the bottom of the sea?...there should not be any invincible obstacle...."

He constantly improved his equipment and with his third camera, a great copper and iron box weighing hundreds of pounds, he made his best pictures.

The camera had to be lowered from a ship to Boutan, who wrestled it into position. He wrote: "Even though the camera,

---

THE AUTHOR: *Luis Marden, Chief of* NATIONAL GEOGRAPHIC's *Foreign Staff, has photographed the ocean world for 25 years. An early specialist in 35mm color work, he published the first book on the subject,* Color Photography with a Miniature Camera, *in 1934. In 1957 he discovered and photographed the bones of Captain Bligh's* Bounty *off Pitcairn Island.*

lighter when submerged, could be handled by one man under water...many times I have worn myself out...the sweat rolled down my forehead; the steam...condensed on the windows of the diving dress, and the landscape was barely perceptible through a dense fog.

"Not having the use of my hands within the helmet, I could do nothing but rub the ...glass with my nose or my tongue...to make a small window through which I could perceive objects more clearly."

Poor perspiring Boutan later made things a bit easier for himself by using an empty wine barrel as a float and suspending the camera from it.

With the slow photographic plates of his day, Boutan found it difficult to make "instantaneous" photographs—snapshots. At best he could only squeeze the shutter open and shut for about 1/50 of a second, barely enough to stop the motion of swimming fish and gorgonians swaying in the current. In despair, he tried a new lamp designed for him by an electrical engineer,

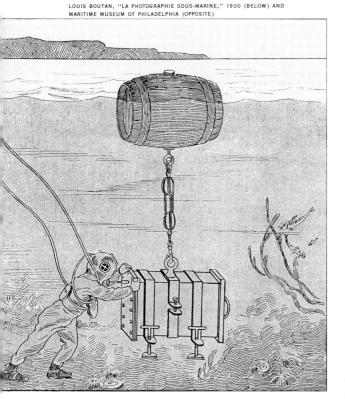

Father of undersea photography, Louis Boutan takes a self-portrait 12 feet down. An empty wine cask buoys his heavy camera (left). In 1892 he photographed a Mediterranean spider crab (opposite), in the first known underwater picture.

one M. Chaufour. It burned a twisted ribbon of magnesium, ignited by a platinum filament that reddened when battery contacts were connected. The magnesium burned unevenly and Boutan gave up the lamp, but the ingenious device was the ancestor of the flashbulb.

Finally, in 1899, after unsuccessful experiments with another lamp, the resourceful Parisian developed an unmanned deep-sea camera, the chief photographic tool of oceanographers today. In glass-and-metal spheres on each side of the housing, he placed arc lights powered by batteries on the vessel above. Opening the shutter by remote control, he made a sharp picture at 160 feet.

Boutan concluded his experiments in 1900. At the end of his book he wrote: ". . . I have opened the way . . . it remains for others to follow me, to open up new paths, and to arrive at ultimate success."

In 1914 English-born J. E. Williamson made the first undersea motion pictures. From a barge he hung a flexible metal tube; through it a man could descend to a steel sphere 30 feet below. Inside the capsule, big enough to hold two men with cameras, dry divers photographed the sea life of Bahama coral reefs through a plate-glass window. From this "photosphere" Williamson made black-and-white and color films.

But the first man to make an extensive series of still pictures of fish in their natural habitat was, so far as I know, Professor William H. Longley, an ichthyologist at Goucher College in Baltimore.

Professor Longley walked the seabed off the Dry Tortugas, a coral islet beyond Key West, Florida, in 1917. He used a Graflex

Patterned hogfish roams sandy shallows of the Gulf of Mexico in an underwater color picture made in 1926 by ichthyologist W. H. Longley and Charles Martin of the National Geographic Society. The Society sponsored such early color endeavors and continues to support experiments in undersea photography. In a 1955 photograph by author Luis Marden, surgeonfish dart among swaying sea whips 200 feet down in the Red Sea.

camera in a beautifully made watertight brass box that I saw many years later in a laboratory of the Smithsonian Institution.

The professor made hundreds of black-and-white photographs, showing for the first time the habits of many fish: a trunkfish blowing sand away from its food, a trumpetfish hiding head down in the plumes of a sea feather, and a host of other things that cannot be learned from shriveled brown specimens preserved in alcohol.

When Dr. Longley submitted an article on life of the coral reef to the NATIONAL GEOGRAPHIC in 1926, the Magazine's editors, who had pioneered in the use of color photographs, thought at once of undersea pictures in color. But the color plates then used by the Society, the Lumière Autochrome, were exceedingly slow. They required a one-second exposure at f/8 even in bright sunlight, and it seemed impossible to photograph moving objects in the weak undersea light.

A T THAT TIME, Charles Martin, an ingenious technician and innovator, headed the National Geographic's Photographic Laboratory. In July of 1926, the Society sent him to Dry Tortugas to collaborate with Dr. Longley. The two soon discovered that, like Boutan, they needed artificial light, lots of it.

More light and moving subjects meant flashlight photography. Before the invention of flashbulbs, flash pictures were made by igniting powdered magnesium with a spark. The quantity normally used was about one ounce, but to record submarine scenes on the Autochrome plates, Martin used an incredible *one pound* per flash, exploded on a raft.

In a letter to the Society, Longley wrote: "I hope we may succeed gloriously, but it is a gamble." It was also dangerous. The powder went off with a blinding flash in a cloud of smoke, lighting the sea bottom with the equivalent of 2,400 flashbulbs, more light than has ever been used, before or since, to make pictures under the sea.

There was no precedent for this kind of photography; Charles Martin had to invent

Firing a Nikonos camera with hand-held and frame-mounted flashes, a photographer takes portraits of plankton, the oceans' tiniest inhabitants, with a close-up lens. Spare flashbulbs float in the net bag. Drifters more than swimmers, plants as well as animals, plankton comprise the basic foodstuff of the sea. Below, left to right: a section of a siphonophore, a jellyfish colony buoyed by gas-filled floats; trochophore, a peanut-worm larva; protozoan, a one-celled animal with tiny whips for beating slowly through the water; acorn-worm larva, a trochophore that spins around as it swims; sea butterfly, a "flying" mollusk, its streamer sensory tentacles extending from winglike feet; and a mollusk veliger larva wrapped in a crystalline membrane.

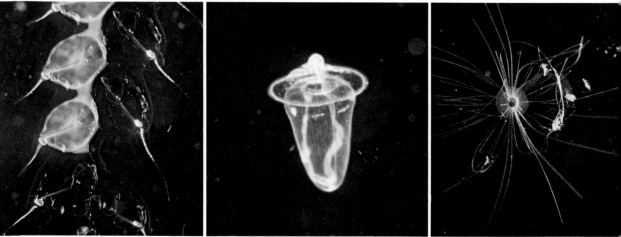

APPROXIMATELY 3 TIMES LIFE-SIZE   APPROXIMATELY 16 TIMES LIFE-SIZE   APPROXIMATELY 16 TIMES LIFE-SIZE

or improvise all his equipment. He built a pontoon raft to carry the powder and the apparatus for firing it. Over the raft he stretched a white cloth to reflect the light downward. Dr. Longley, walking 10 to 15 feet below, towed the light raft about as he moved. Martin even devised the synchronizer that would fire the powder when the camera shutter opened.

When he returned to Washington, he could report triumphantly: "Herewith are eight autochromes of genuine sub-marine life; the first ones ever taken."

They were also the first undersea color photographs ever published. They appeared in the January, 1927, NATIONAL GEOGRAPHIC, and marked a milestone in the history of photography. Nearly 30 years passed before the publication of another undersea color photograph.

After World War II ended, the Aqua-Lung came on the world market, and increasing numbers of amateur divers began to go down into the sea. At once they tried to take cameras with them, to show the stay-on-lands what the clamor was all about. The first problem was simply that of keeping the camera dry. All kinds of clever makeshifts appeared, from cameras encased in Mason jars to cameras looking through a glass port in rubber hotwater bottles. Only a few divers had the skill or means to attempt a proper case of metal or plastic through which camera controls of

film advance, focus, iris diaphragm, and shutter speeds would be workable.

By that time I had obtained my first commercial underwater housing, a sea-green metal cylinder made in Venice. For some time I had been trying to make color photographs under the sea, but there was a hitch. Martin and Longley had taken their color pictures in crystalline water 10 to 15 feet deep. Lighted by that stupendous flash overhead, the brilliant color of the coral reef came through faithfully. But as depth increases, the thickening blue-green filter of seawater, interposed between the sunlight and the bottom, absorbs the colors of the spectrum. First the reds, then the oranges and yellows, disappear, until beyond 30 feet or so, the diver walks or swims in a monochromatic blue-green world.

In shallow clear water, the eye adjusts to the prevailing blue and can still see some reds and yellows, darkened and degraded from their surface brilliance. My first pictures disappointed me, because they looked like black-and-white photographs tinted blue-green. Unlike the human eye, the photographic emulsion does not possess the power of adaptation, and all the warm colors were drowned in blue light.

I used correcting filters to hold back the excessive blue, and got fairly good photographs in the limpid waters of the Mediterranean, provided I did not go too deep. But I soon learned that to make really good

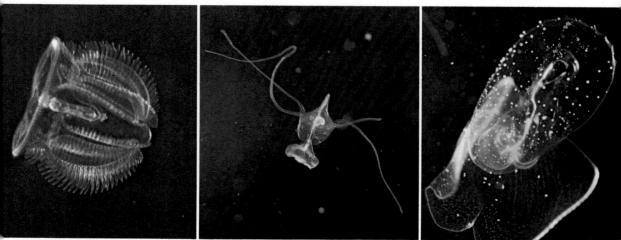

APPROXIMATELY 16 TIMES LIFE-SIZE   APPROXIMATELY 4 TIMES LIFE-SIZE   APPROXIMATELY 20 TIMES LIFE-SIZE

color pictures underwater I had to use an artificial light source close to the subject. Flashbulbs seemed ideal, and in 1955 when I accompanied Captain Cousteau aboard *Calypso* during his filming of *The Silent World,* I took along 600 of them.

Cousteau later recalled our experience: "Our divers wonder how a man can fire that many bulbs in only four months. They soon discover how. Hardly have we left the Suez Canal before Marden begins diving with stout Émile Robert as bearer.

"Robert goes down carrying Marden's second camera and a large string bag of flashbulbs, which floats above him like the envelope of an 18th-century balloon. It is not long before Marden is crying for more bulbs and we radio for a fresh supply.

"The bulbs, when under pressure, develop leaks in the metal bases. Water seeps inside, short-circuits the lead-in wires, and makes firing uncertain.

"Marden is chagrined, but the *Calypso* team comes to his rescue. At night we see a strange scene in the mess. The ship's cook heats water; the second cook melts wax in the water; my wife, Simone, cleans the bulb bases; the engineer drills two tiny holes in the base of each bulb; and at the end of the production line stands the ship's young surgeon in his white tunic. With the delicacy of a brain surgeon he injects liquid wax into the holes to insulate the wires.

"Luis's expenditure of bulbs taxes the production rate: It is a race between manufacturer and consumer. We treat 2,500 bulbs before the voyage is over."

Most of them worked. But at depths of a hundred feet or so, something else happened: The bulbs sometimes imploded, shattering violently inward, instead of outward as in an explosion, and driving the fragments of glass into my gloved hand like bullets. The pure oxygen that fills flashbulbs is at a pressure less than one atmosphere, so their thin glass walls undergo strain even at relatively shallow depths. After firing weakened the glass by developing minute cracks in it, some bulbs imploded when touched.

This happened to me the first time as I

Weightless as astronauts, technicians test a simulate

swam above a sunken ship at 90 feet in the Red Sea. When I took hold of the bulb to remove it from the reflector, I heard a dull report and felt a numbing pain lance through my right thumb. A wisp of greenish "smoke" slowly curled upward; it was my blood, drained of its bright red at this depth.

NATIONAL GEOGRAPHIC PHOTOGRAPHER BATES W. LITTLEHALES

anned Apollo space station in the Caribbean Sea. A 90-degree lens shows the entire 56-foot structure.

Weeks later, when another implosion left a neat scar on the middle finger of my right hand, tracing the exact curve of the big bulb, I started to search for some kind of protective glove. But the stoutest leather was ineffective against the tremendous impact of the shattering glass. A chain-mail glove made for butchers provided the answer. Now I handle even the jagged bases of shattered bulbs with impunity.

It is an uncannily beautiful sight to look at a calm sea on a dark night when underwater photographers are at work. Suddenly and silently a circle of sea a hundred feet in diameter briefly flashes firefly green, like heat lightning on the horizon. Three-

101

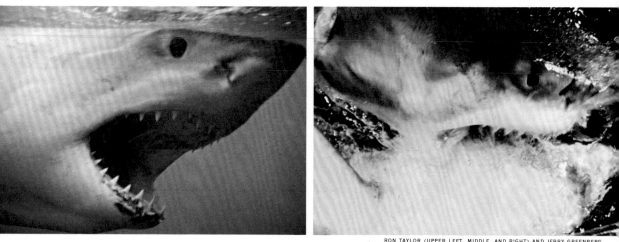

Savage jaws agape, a great white shark bares two-inch dagger-sharp teeth seconds before assaulting and devouring a dead shark tied to an Australian fishing boat. A movie camera record- *ed the swift attack. Below, seven-foot bull sharks and a pup search for prey along the edge of a reef in the Florida Keys. When hunting, the slow-moving bulls sometimes enter rivers. Armed with*

an aluminum "bangstick," a diver challenges a danger-
ous white-tipped shark. This lightweight weapon fires a
12-gauge shotgun shell when jammed against a solid
object. To assure a kill, the diver aims for the brain.

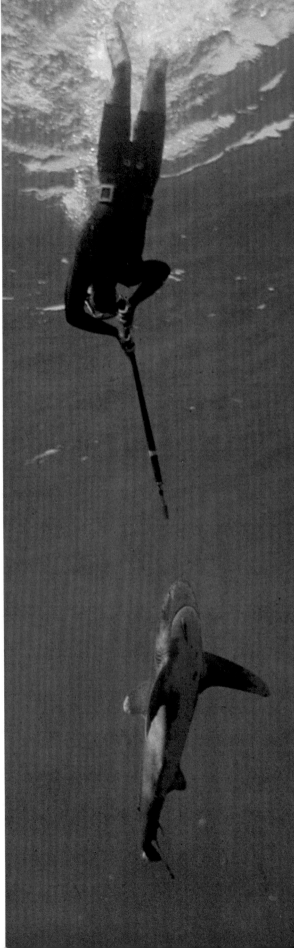

quarters of a century ago, Louis Boutan's skipper noted the awesome effect of the professor's submarine flashes. "It is as though a storm is raging under the sea," he said.

As a result of Cousteau's expedition I discovered another problem with color. While swimming 60 feet down in the Indian Ocean, I had seen a clump of sea anemones with globular tentacles like bunches of brilliant red grapes. I took several flash pictures, but the film lay undeveloped until several months later. Then I was disappointed and puzzled, for the tentacles had photographed a muddy brown. Thinking back, I deduced what had happened.

In the bright blue daylight the anemones were fluorescing, and to my eye, they had looked bright red. But when my flash fired, the reddish artificial light did not excite fluorescence, and the film recorded only the brown surface coloration.

If I had had my wits about me, I would have realized that normally one cannot see reds at 60 feet. What I was looking at is now a well-known phenomenon, but apparently the NATIONAL GEOGRAPHIC article of February, 1956, was the first published account of underwater observation and photography of submarine biofluorescence.

Anyone who has ever thrust his mask-enclosed face under water knows all divers have big feet. And big hands, too. That is, they look bigger when seen through a diving mask. Because of the difference in refraction of light rays passing from water to the air inside the diver's viewing mask, everything underwater appears about 30 percent bigger than life.

Things look bigger and closer to the camera lens as well, so to restore objects

Flipped onto its back (upper left), a blue starfish rights itself by turning a slow somersault on the seabed off Queensland, Australia. Mating cuttlefish entwine tentacles in a rare underwater photograph near New Caledonia in the South Pacific. Related to the squid and octopus, a cuttlefish camouflages itself by changing color in two-thirds of a second, or screens itself with a brown-black ink used by artists for pigment.

DOUGLAS FAULKNER. STARFISH 1/6 LIFE-SIZE; CUTTLEFISH LIFE-SIZE

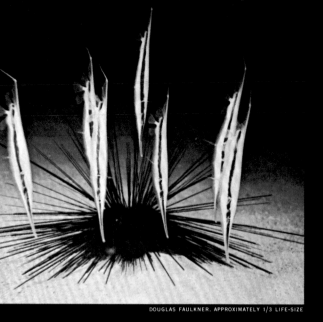

Bizarre patterns of the sea: Tawny blotches of a Sargassum fish (above) merge with weeds in a floating meadow of the Sargasso Sea. Featherlike shrimpfish swim head-down among prickly spines of a black sea urchin. Purplemouth moray eels, a menace to divers, bare needlelike teeth, and a translucent jellyfish trails delicate but deadly stinging tentacles. Bunched like a cluster of matches, nubby tentacles of a sea anemone shelter a spidery cleaner shrimp. A gaudy sea slug inches above coral polyps, and a silvery seahorse roams reef coral. The Nassau grouper scowls like a bulldog and, when hooked, fights like one.

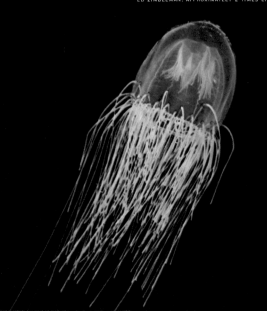

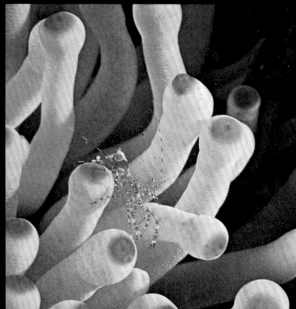

to normal size and to maintain a full field of view, correcting lenses have been designed to replace the flat glass portholes of most camera housings. The correction can be made by curved glass, which all light rays strike at approximately a right angle, causing no distortion; a better corrector may be made of two lenses in combination.

Some panoramic view masks with a curved plate give a sort of wide-screen effect. I tried one flat plate with slanting sides that gave me the impression I was continuously swimming in a steep-sided trench.

The average diving mask makes the diver feel like a horse in blinders; he can see straight ahead, but has no vision at the sides. Sometimes this can be frightening.

Once, in the Indian Ocean, as I bent over to focus my camera, something whipped over my left shoulder and hit the flash reflector with a resounding clang. I nearly spat out my mouthpiece in fright, thinking it might be a shark or barracuda. When the fish turned and came toward me, I recognized it as a big, harmless jack. The polished parabolic reflector must have attracted the fish by sending moons of light glancing through the water, like the wobbling chromed spoon of a trolling fisherman.

One of the underwater photographer's most valuable tools is the electronic flash invented by Dr. Harold E. Edgerton, a witty and brilliant Professor of Electrical Measurements at the Massachusetts Institute of Technology. In 1931, Dr. Edgerton, seeking a method of freezing the motion of high-speed machinery, built a flashing stroboscopic lamp bright enough to

Hunting algae and small invertebrates, scaleless orangespot filefish skim past a cluster of staghorn coral in the Indian Ocean. The tubelike mouth of the three-inch fish contains incisor teeth that can nip off hard-shelled barnacles. Soft, pastel coral polyps build limestone homes throughout earth's warm seas. Fluorescing coral (top) reveals tiny rivulets of color. Cactuslike pillar coral (center) grows in spiny clumps, and maze coral (bottom) forms a network of twisting corridors.

photograph by, and the high-speed electronic flash was born.

Through development and refinement, the instrument lost weight and its flash increased in brilliance. The flash—as brief as 1/100,000 of a second or less—could stop such high-speed motion as the wings of a bird in flight or the swing of a golf club.

Dimitri Rebikoff, a French engineer, adapted an electronic flash of his design to underwater use in 1949. He enclosed a lamp and mechanism in a long plexiglass tube filled with clear oil to withstand pressure that otherwise might crush the tube. With this instrument, the submerged cameraman was free of the fragile and bothersome flash bulbs that not only tended to bite the hand that held them but also flew upward to the surface if they escaped from the net bag.

In 1951 I went to M.I.T., to confer with Dr. Edgerton about his high-speed photographs of hummingbirds. Somehow we began to talk of my long love affair with the undersea world, and Dr. Edgerton said, "For a long time I have had an idea for an unmanned deep-sea camera knocking around in my head." He described an automatic camera synchronized with a flashing strobe light that would take 500 pictures at a charge.

After I returned to Washington, I told Melville Bell Grosvenor, of the National Geographic Society, about the professor's idea. The Society's Research Committee subsequently furnished Dr. Edgerton with support to build and to experiment with the deep-sea automatic camera.

When the abyssal camera was ready, Dr. Grosvenor introduced Professor Edgerton to Captain Cousteau. The ebullient crew of *Calypso* quickly dubbed the inventor of the strobe light "Papa Flash."

At first the professor lowered the camera and a cylinder holding the flash mechanism on deep-sea trawling wires, but the wires were heavy and tended to break.

One wire snapped while a camera hung some three miles down on the north wall of the Puerto Rico Trench. Dr. Edgerton carefully noted the latitude and longitude, and

Ivory-tusked Pacific walruses pack a stony beach on Walrus Island, Alaska. The ponderous mammals rarely venture out to sea, preferring coastal

STEVE McCUTCHEON (ABOVE); BILL DE COURT (RIGHT); AND ALAN ROOT

shallows. Their southern cousins, the frolicsome sea lions (below) ride a sparkling comber shoreward in the Galapagos Islands. Streamlined right up to its whiskers, the wide-eyed sea lion has perfect form for body surfing.

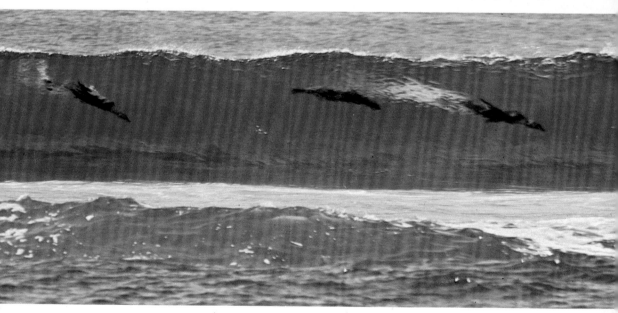

the following year went back to look for it.

"We welded together all the scrap angle iron we could find on the ship," he recalls, "to make a snagging grapnel. Three miles of wire had gone down with the camera and I thought we might hook the tangle. We dragged the area all night, and then reeled in the wire. It took an hour to bring it up, and all we found wedged in the grapnel was one piece of coal. But my name and address are clearly marked on the camera, so, if anyone finds it, will he please send it back to me?"

The weight of three miles of wire alone can be enough to cause it to snap, not to mention the added drag of the equipment on the end of it. To circumvent this, Dr. Edgerton came up with the idea of using a line of nylon, which has the same specific gravity as water and therefore would have no weight when submerged. It worked perfectly. In fact, when a camera caught on the bottom several thousand feet down, the highly elastic line actually pulled the 360-ton *Calypso* backward.

All the ship's company helped as Cousteau and Dr. Edgerton built an ingenious device in 1953. They turned a metal ladder into "a purely impromptu invention," the sea sled. The ladder's handrails served as runners when the ship towed it along the sea floor, and the camera strapped to its rungs ultimately took thousands of pictures of the bottom and its creatures.

Techniques and equipment have improved since the early experiments. Nowadays an echo sounder measures the distance to the bottom, enabling the surface operators to place a camera precisely with relation to the seabed. But "Papa Flash" is still dissatisfied with the area of sea bottom covered by his cameras.

"Under the sea," he says, "the weather is always bad. At the very best, with super-

Creeping in bottom ooze more than a mile down off Cape Cod, a sea spider, lighted by an electronic flash

clear conditions, an underwater camera seldom can be used even at 100 feet from the subject or the bottom. The light-scattering and absorption effects of the water act as fog does over land.

"A mapping aircraft can cover an area of 20 square miles from an altitude of 30,000 feet. Until recently, most deep-ocean photography was being done ten feet from the bottom, covering about 50 square feet at each exposure. If we could raise the cameras and take pictures from 30 feet, we could then take in 500 square feet of sea floor at a time."

Even at this rate, to photograph the continental shelves would take more than 500

Pioneer of deep-sea lights and cameras, Dr. Harold E. Edgerton of the Massachusetts Institute of Technology lowers an early model strobe into a "pressure pot" for tests at simulated depth.

...sts a shadow over a five-pointed brittle star; a deep-sea fish, propelled by its whiplike tail, forages for food.

HAROLD E. EDGERTON; FROM WOODS HOLE OCEANOGRAPHIC INSTITUTION. APPROXIMATE SIZES: SEA SPIDER 1/2 LIFE-SIZE; DEEP-SEA FISH 1/2 LIFE-SIZE

billion exposures. Still, somehow the task must be done if man is to utilize fully these zones for fish farming, submarine agriculture, and mining.

Dimitri Rebikoff has designed Pegasus, a fascinating nine-foot-long torpedolike gadget powered by an electric motor. It "flies" like a tiny aircraft, whether operated by a diver stretched out atop its hull or remotely controlled. Cameras on Pegasus open their shutters in synchronization with a flashing strobe light to photograph strips of sea bed.

These applications of the unmanned abyssal camera are of immense importance, but as a working journalist, my first love goes to the hand-held cameras that I can use to make photographs of the strange beauty of the drowned world. Such equipment has come a long way since my experiments in the 1940's.

Dr. Edgerton recently designed powerful hand strobe units that work either directly in synchronization with the camera, or fire remotely, triggered by a photoelectric cell. And a Belgian engineer, M. Jean de Wouters, has developed the world's first amphibious camera, the Nikonos. This small 35mm camera needs no housing because it is itself waterproof, like a diver's watch.

The ocean deeps are the least-known parts of the earth, and creatures undreamed of in our zoology may well dwell there. Only recently have scientists given some measure of serious attention to "sea serpents." Of the hundreds of sightings over the centuries, many were too well-documented to be dismissed.

In 1930 Danish scientist Anton Bruun, trawling from the ship *Dana* off the Cape of Good Hope, brought up an astounding creature, long, flat, and translucent, with a diminutive head. It was a leptocephalus, the larva of an eel. In this stage most eels reach no more than four inches in length. But the leptocephalus hauled up in *Dana's* net was *six feet* long. If the larva continued to grow at the same rate as the common eel, the adult creature's length might have been as much as 70 feet.

Is this the Great Sea Serpent of yarns told by thousands of seamen down the centuries? I think it is, and one day an Edgerton camera, flashing in the abyssal blackness every 15 seconds, may well give us a portrait, beyond doubt at last, of the most storied sea creature of all.

WALTER MEAYERS EDWARDS, NATIONAL GEOGRAPHIC STAFF (BELOW) AND HAROLD E. EDGERTON AND JACQUES-YVES COUSTEAU

Sea sled improvised by Cousteau (in blue shirt) and his crew swings aboard Calypso, *anchored in Nice Harbor, France. Forerunner of more sophisticated models, the sled supported an Edgerton camera and strobe synchronized to click every 15 seconds while being towed along the bottom. Holes drilled in the tubular frame admitted seawater to equalize the deep pressures. Bumping along at 10,000 feet, the apparatus lighted a lava-studded valley (opposite) of the Mid-Atlantic Ridge.*

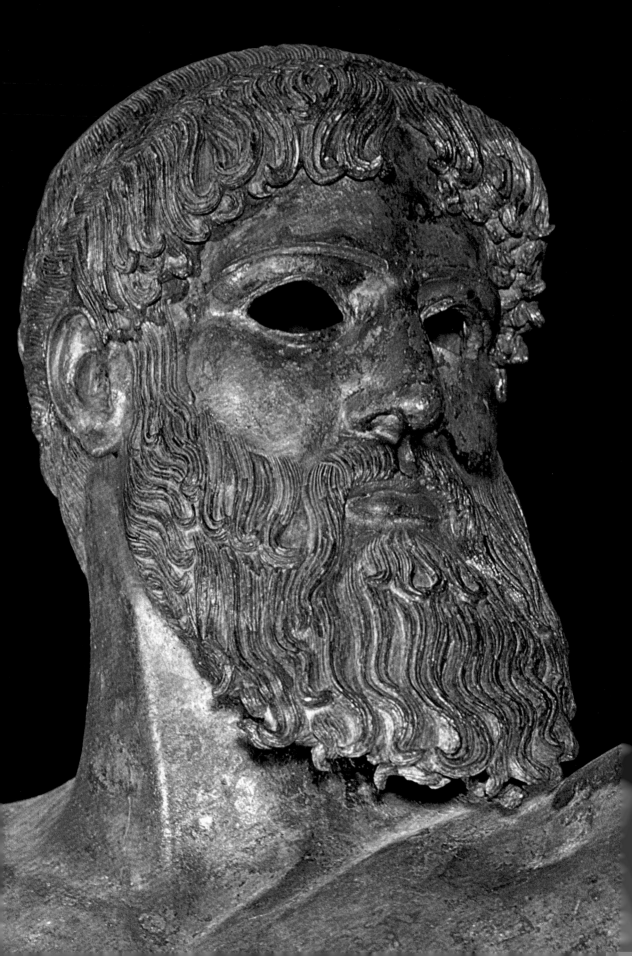

6

The Sea's Dark Museum

BY JAMES DUGAN

Bronze Poseidon, or possibly Zeus, bears the patina of 2,300 years' immersion in the Aegean Sea. Divers in 1928 brought up the Greek masterwork off Cape Artemision. It now stands in the National Archaeological Museum, Athens.

I CLUNG to *Calypso*'s rail one bright summer day in 1953 as she bucked the Mediterranean along a desolate chain of white rocks that had ripped open scores of ships. Captain Cousteau had set his research vessel on a course for a rendezvous with one of the victims—a Greek wine freighter that failed to arrive in Massalia (present-day Marseille) about 230 B.C.

A mooring buoy marked her grave. She lay keel down, her stern at 112 feet and her bow at 140 feet, on the sloping pedestal of a barren stone island called Grand Congloué, about ten miles east of Marseille.

Uninhabited before, Grand Congloué now boasted the newest village in France. Here Cousteau directed the most extensive marine archeological dig yet tackled.

This settlement, christened Port Calypso, consisted of an enginehouse perched 15 feet above the water and connected by an iron ladder rooted in the cliff to a yellow tin house on a ledge above. An 85-foot spar stretched out from the enginehouse. On the end of the spar, an air-lift hose twisted 140 feet down into the sea. The powerful hose sucked up sediment and deposited it on shore, where Cousteau's men carefully sifted it for artifacts.

"What a struggle Frédéric Dumas and I had to perfect this suction pump," Cousteau said. "But it works. Like sculptors we use it to carve amphorae [wine jars] free from the silt covering the wreck. It literally devours the bottom sediments like a vacuum sweeper."

Cousteau's five-year project began in August, 1952, when he dived near Grand Congloué, acting on a tip that "old pots" lay just off the island's forbidding cliffs. Professor Fernand Benoît, director of the Marseille Archeological Museum, accompanied him on *Calypso* to identify whatever pottery he might bring up.

Cousteau ventured 220 feet down the sides of a sandy slope, but found nothing. "I doubled back around the fateful cape," he said, "growing tired and much disappointed. Then at 200 feet I found an amphora. A single specimen is meaningless; it could have been accidentally lost at

Derrick

Engine
House

Suction
Pipe

Wreck's Anchor
Lodged on Shelf

112 feet

Deck
Cleared

Stern Excavated

Partly Excavated
Bow Sections

Pottery
Mound

Gunwales

140 feet

sea. So I ascended another 60 feet and suddenly I was alongside a high tumulus of sand and rubble, looking at a cascade of broken pottery. A lolling dogfish grudgingly gave way to let me work loose a stack of three cups resembling chalices."

His air supply almost gone, Cousteau surfaced thrusting the three cups ahead of him. "They're Campanian!" cried Benoît, who had found similar cups in France dating from the 2d century B.C.

Cousteau pledged *Calypso* for two months' work at the site. Later he wrote: "How naive that schedule seems now! The wreck was to take five years and the life of Jean-Pierre Serventi, a young diver who had a fatal stroke at 220 feet. The ancient ship had made war on us."

But scientists and scholars hailed the Grand Congloué project as the first important underwater excavation. Cousteau's innovations, such as the use of free divers and the air lift, promised significant advances in archeology. Support came from both public and private sources, including the National Geographic Society.

Cousteau rotated two-man teams on the bottom and used underwater TV cameras to relay their operations to *Calypso*'s cabin. "Our new window on the sea was a revelation to archeologists on board," he said.

Divers found the jars stacked upright. "Wet amphorae arrived on deck coruscating in the sun," Cousteau reported. "Their purple and gold biological encrustation faded soon into dun and drab and dried into a patina of white fossils and iodine stains where shellfish had been attached."

Some amphorae had two stamps impressed into their lips—"SES" in Roman letters, followed by an anchor symbol.

Diver 120 feet down inspects a jumble of amphorae, or wine jars, spilled from a Greek merchantman that sank about 230 B.C. near Massalia (modern Marseille). In 1952 the National Geographic— Calypso *Marine Archeological Expedition began salvaging some 3,000 amphorae from the cargo. Calypso (left) anchors above the site off Grand Congloué Island.*

Others bore the same initials and a trident. From clues found in ancient stone epigraphs, Benoît tentatively identified the "trademarks" as those of Marcus Sestius, a Roman merchant given honorary citizenship by the Greek isle of Delos in 240 B.C.

Cousteau and I visited Delos, where we chanced upon the ruins of a villa with an elegant mosaic floor. A bold trident caught our attention. The tines formed an E bracketing two S's. This struck us as a variation of the SES on the wine jars! Furthermore, volcanic pebbles in the courtyard matched some found in the wreck. The chief archeologist at Delos responded to our excitement with a skeptical smile, but Cousteau and I would always believe we had indeed visited Sestius' villa.

Excavations at Grand Congloué yielded more than 6,000 pieces of black Campanian pottery and thousands of amphorae. The divers lifted many parts of the ship, including 200 tons of lead sheathing. In the stern they found a small earthenware stove, and gear presumably belonging to the crew. Surprisingly, not a single coin or any item of precious metal turned up.

Cousteau's commitment in both time and money at Grand Congloué almost wrecked his oceanographic study program, and he abandoned Port Calypso in 1957. "The rock returned to solitude and the gulls," he wrote later. "It bears no evidence now of human occupation save for a rusting ladder on the wall of the eastern cape and a plaque bearing the name of Jean-Pierre Serventi."

For thousands of years divers have visited sunken wrecks in the Mediterranean, seeing worth only in sponges and corals

Substituting air for brawn, divers recover ages-old cargo near Turkey. The balloon lifts a sea-welded mass of copper ingots and bronze tools from the oldest shipwreck known — a Bronze Age trading vessel that sank in 90 feet of water off Cape Gelidonya 32 centuries ago. Buoyed by air from a diver's Aqua-Lung, the amphora (below), part of a wine shipment lost near Yassi Island, will rocket to the surface when released.

JOHN COCHRAN (BELOW) AND HERB GREER

Bronze Age relics lie in sunlight after three millenniums in the sea. Artifacts from the

and leaving amphorae and other artifacts on the bottom to gather bright crusts of sea life. Archeologists sorrowfully contemplate the many remnants of ancient cargoes that fishing nets must have brought up in the past, particularly the classical sculptures. At painfully long intervals a few somehow found their way to museums; most were destroyed by ignorance and cupidity. Bronze figures had scrap value and were melted down in furnaces. Marble statuary was either burned for lime or piled on breakwaters.

In 1900 a fortuitous event altered the destiny of the sea's priceless relics. Shortly before Easter, a gale forced two sponging caïques to lie to under a cliff on Andikíthira Island, northwest of Crete. An enterprising diver, Elias Stadiatis, took advantage of the layover to scout for sponges in this unfamiliar territory. Dropping down some 180 feet, the helmeted intruder was amazed to find himself surrounded by an awesome array: huge white horses, nude figures, and oversize bronze arms and legs torn loose from their torsos. He signaled

Cape Gelidonya wreck include bronze picks, chisels, axes, and copper "oxhides"—possibly used as money. Expedition director George Bass and his wife apply plastic preservatives to bits of wood from the ship. Mrs. Bass delicately brushes the largest piece of recovered timber.

"up" on his line and broke through the surface carrying a large bronze arm.

The captain, Demetrios Kondos, himself a master diver, went down for a look at the strange scene. That day marked a turning point in underwater archeology. When the captain reported his discovery in Athens, the Greek government supported a mission including Kondos's helmet divers, an archeologist, and a navy vessel. Today the finds of the expedition are among the treasures of the National Archaeological Museum in Athens.

Kondos's men raised a splendid bronze god or athlete of the 4th century B.C., two smaller bronzes dating from the 5th century B.C., and marble fragments of a much later period. Seawater and an overlay of shells had defaced many of the marble statues. The bronzes had fared better.

How did one ship happen to carry a collection ranging over several centuries? The answer probably lies in the twisted bases of the bronze figures, which suggest they had been roughly torn off their stone bases. Scholars think the wreck was a Roman

plunder ship that sank in the 1st century B.C. after the looting of Athens.

Among the smaller finds lay the dials, gear wheels, and inscribed plates of a bronze mechanism, soon recognized as some kind of astronomical device. Experts at the Greek National Museum patiently cleaned its fragments until fine details appeared. In 1959, Dr. Derek J. de Solla Price, Professor of the History of Science at Yale, announced that it probably served as a computer for calculating the motions of stars and planets quickly and easily. Certainly, it proves unexpected mastery of scientific technology in Hellenistic Greece. Dr. Price says: "Nothing like this instrument is preserved elsewhere."

Sponge divers also found one of the glories of the Greek national collections: the magnificent bronze figure of Poseidon, or possibly Zeus, raised in 1928 near Cape Artemísion, about 75 miles north of Athens. Later Greece presented an exact copy to the United Nations in New York.

124

At the same site divers rescued a small bronze jockey and the forepart of his rearing steed—a work of superb naturalism and charm. Professor George Karo of the German School of Athens, who had organized the art salvage, said to me long afterward: "I cannot tell you of the anguish I felt when a diver's death, inadequate equipment, and lack of funds forced me to break off further excavations." And in nearly 40 years no one has returned to look for more masterpieces in the watery cache off Artemísion.

But antiquities abound in the Mediterranean and the Aegean. No one knows this better than Peter Throckmorton. In 1958, as a young photojournalist with archeological experience, he spent the summer aboard a Turkish sponge boat owned by Captain Kemâl Aras. During the cruise, he recorded the sites of more than 30 sunken ships. The captain mentioned another not scheduled for a visit on this trip—a bronze-littered wreck off Turkey's southwest coast. Recognizing its importance, Throckmorton noted the details in his log.

The following summer he joined a diving expedition in Turkish waters organized

Straddling scaffolding 100 feet down, a diver photographs timbers of a Byzantine merchantman wrecked near Yassi Island 1,300 years ago. Iron grids enable archeologists to plot the vessel's size and type. For centuries, heavily laden trading ships swarmed among the islands off the Turkish coast, and Yassi's treacherous reef claimed at least a dozen of them.

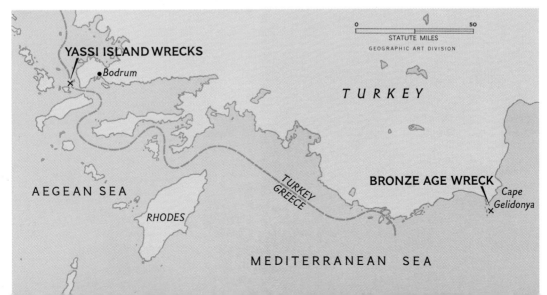

YASSI ISLAND WRECKS
• Bodrum

TURKEY

0   50
STATUTE MILES
GEOGRAPHIC ART DIVISION

TURKEY
GREECE

BRONZE AGE WRECK
Cape
Gelidonya

AEGEAN SEA

RHODES

MEDITERRANEAN SEA

by Drayton Cochran, a New York yachtsman. Heeding Captain Aras's instructions, the divers finally spotted the object of their search—a ship that had struck a jumble of rocks off Cape Gelidonya 32 centuries ago. She sank in 90 feet of water long before Homer composed the *Odyssey*.

I vividly recall Peter's excitement when he turned up in New York with the news. "We have shown pictures and drawings of the wreck to scholars at the University of Pennsylvania and Princeton, and they all say she's late Bronze Age—about 1200 B.C.," he told me. "That would make her the oldest sunken ship ever found!"

Peter sought support for an excavation and got it readily from the University of Pennsylvania Museum, where he met archeologist George F. Bass. George, appointed expedition director, agreed that

Research vessel for underwater archeologists, Asherah — named for the Phoenician sea goddess — prowls for sunken ships off Turkey. The two-man submarine reaches depths of 600 feet. Built for the University of Pennsylvania with grants from the National Geographic Society and the National Science Foundation, the sub can photograph a shipwreck site in hours — a task that takes divers many weeks. Undersea artist with graphite crayon and a sheet of frosted plastic (opposite) plots wine jars at the Yassi Island wreck, before the building of Asherah. Archeologists topside, using divers' drawings and photographs, chart the cargo. Relics tagged for identification head for the surface (right).

Bronze bar, chain, and hooks from the Yassi Island wreck form a steelyard, used by Byzantine traders for weighing cargo. The scale, almost identical to those seen throughout Turkey today, carried a lead-filled counterweight — a ten-inch bust of the goddess Athena.

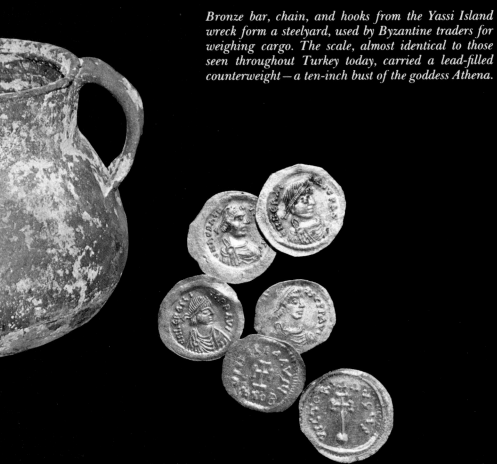

Still intact after 13 centuries on the ocean floor, an earthenware plate, ribbed cup, and wine pitcher served the captain at his table. Resin lining of the jar prevented it from sweating. Clay "wine thief," a type of pipette, drew wine from amphorae. Cooking pot (far left) lay in the galley area. Gold coins of the Byzantine Emperor Heraclius, who reigned A.D. 610-641, indicate the ship sank during the first half of the seventh century.

some of the ship's hull might still exist. If they could recover parts of it, they might find answers to many questions about Bronze Age ships.

I sat up nights with Peter and George as they discussed plans to liberate secrets locked in the sea for more than three millenniums. Peter did not play down the rugged task they faced. "There's no suitable campsite near the wreck. We'll have to dive from a sponge boat and live an hour away."

In the summer of 1960 they camped on a sliver of beach under a forbidding cliff that shed rocks from its heights. As the summer wore on, waves often flooded the camp and water ran under the cots. They

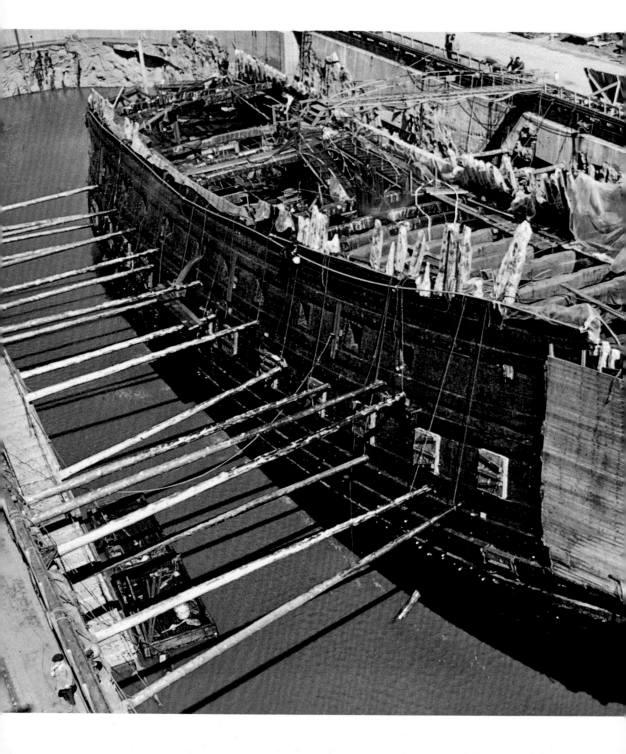

Swedish warship Vasa *sets sail in Stockholm Harbor on her maiden voyage, August 10, 1628. Less than a mile from her quay she capsized and sank in 100 feet of water when hit by a gust of wind. Pontoons, fixed to the keel by divers, helped raise her in 1961 and carry her into dry dock at nearby Beckholmen, where restoration began.*

felt the spite of the *meltem,* a northerly wind that sweeps the Aegean Sea and may have sent the old freighter to her grave.

The cosmopolitan diving corps — from France, the United States, Turkey, Germany, and England — included Frédéric Dumas, by now a veteran of several undersea excavations. Under George's direction they plotted the wreck site and marked its features with numbered plastic tags before photographing them. They cleared away loose material, finding that most of the cargo and the ship's remains were embedded in solid rock and covered with a limestone growth as thick as eight inches.

"As we hacked away at these seeming 'boulders' we discovered them to be full

131

Wheeled gun carriages stand empty on Vasa's *lower gun deck. When the doomed ship heeled over in the wind, water cascaded through these open ports, taking the ship down like a stone. In the 1660's salvors ventured down in crude diving bells to recover 53 of her 64 cannon. Cold, brackish waters of the Baltic Sea preserved the prize for 300 years. Repeated sprinkling prevented too-rapid drying of her heavy oak planks.*

of metal," Peter told me. "In some places ingots lay stacked five deep. Instead of the expected few hundred pounds of objects, we faced tons of material cemented in solid rock.

"The essence of archeology," he continued, "is not merely to dig up objects, but to learn how they are related to each other on the site. This means patient, fussy measuring—and digging without damaging. We needed a shortcut."

Dumas had an answer. "It would be easier to raise big hunks of the boulders and let topside people take them apart," he said. He suggested they try a hydraulic jack to break up the boulders. It took them three days of chiseling to fit the jack under the first mass and snap it off.

"When Dumas lashed a sling around the chunk and attached the steel wire to the winch on the sponge boat above, we felt so great," Peter said, "that we swam somersaults up the line."

This 300-pound morsel of history broke down into stacks of four-cornered copper ingots shaped like oxhides. They had come from Cyprus—whose name gives us the word "copper"—and some carried foundry marks. Bronze tools bore the as yet undeciphered script of late Bronze Age Cyprus.

The divers found a cylinder seal, scarabs, and a series of graduated weights. Portions of baskets and brushwood had withstood 3,200 years of immersion. In one summer, the devoted group performed a classic feat. They deposited a ton of bronze and copper artifacts to Turkey's scientific credit in the Crusader Castle at Bodrum.

The following summer, in 1961, with support from the National Geographic

Society, George Bass assembled a second group to excavate another vessel charted by Peter, by then a research assistant at the University Museum in Philadelphia. This time the target was a merchantman lying off the Turkish coast in the treacherous reefs near Yassi Island.

"We planned to proceed underwater just as archeologists work on land," George said, "digging down layer by layer, carefully recording the position of each object before moving or raising it. To make sense

of what we found, it was essential that we assemble a detailed plan of the ship and what it held."

Frederick van Doorninck, Jr., a young archeology student, assumed responsibility for fitting together all the data at the site. His work would enable the expedition to re-create the vessel on paper, plank by plank and nail by nail.

George found it much easier to train archeologists to be divers than the other way around. His expedition, with several archeology students, consisted of a cinematographer, still photographers, a diving instructor, an artist, an architect, and a surgeon—a team any land excavation force would envy.

The hapless ship lay, at its deepest point, in about 120 feet of water, 30 feet deeper than the Bronze Age vessel. The increased depth meant the archeologists had to go down to about the limit for effective Aqua-Lung work. U. S. Navy diving tables indicated the dives must be set for no more

than 43 minutes a day, in two separate dives with three- to six-hour intervals between. So, four divers could do only three man-hours of work a day.

At first, the men-fish sketched objects with graphite crayons on frosted plastic sheets. Then they worked out a far better mapping technique. Fifteen divers spent the better part of two weeks building a unique time-saving device that George described this way: "First, we placed a scaffolding of pipe and angle iron over the entire wreck. To accommodate to the slope of the site, we arranged the scaffolding in nine giant steps to hold a 13-foot-high camera tower. Thus we could take grid photographs quickly at each step of the scaffolding. We could plot planks and nail holes to the exact centimeter. This practi-

cally eliminated the lengthy, tedious process of underwater drawing."

One day a diver brought up a gold coin bearing the profile of Heraclius, the Byzantine emperor who ruled from A.D. 610 to 641. "We kept finding more coins with the profile of Heraclius," George reported. "Therefore, I thought it a safe bet that the wreck was of a Byzantine ship built during the first half of the seventh century."

As the divers swam the 65-foot length of the visible wreckage, they came upon six iron anchors cemented together by corrosion and each the height of a man. They could see the strewn cargo of nearly 1,000 amphorae. Near the stern lay terra cotta shards from the galley roof and objects from the captain's personal possessions.

The excavators dispatched fragile articles

PAINTING BY NATIONAL GEOGRAPHIC ARTIST ROBERT W. NICHOLSON

Shattered by earthquake, the buccaneer city of Port Royal slides into the sea as walls collapse and yawning cracks trap fleeing men and women. Within two minutes on the morning of June 7, 1692, two-thirds of the Jamaican town and 2,000 of its inhabitants vanished. In 1959 divers explored the drowned port, helping to recover hundreds of relics. Edwin A. Link, inventor of the Link Trainer for student flyers, and an underwater explorer, led the expedition, sponsored in part by the National Geographic Society.

four hours spent each day in going to and from Bodrum.

Uncovering what was left of the ship, the divers found that the iron nails holding the hull together had rusted away. To keep the wood from floating off in the current, they bought 2,000 bicycle-wheel spokes and pinned the wood firmly to the sand. Soon, a significant fact came to light: The ship's planks were not edge-joined as in the earlier Roman ships. They were nailed to frames in the modern way, and then probably calked. The derelict represented the earliest evidence of modern ship construction.

Sometimes, in moments of excessive greed, Neptune has scorned mere ships, claiming the very land itself to enrich his realm. These acts of plunder have given archeologists some of their most irresistible challenges. I share the hopes of those who search for such legendary places as the sunken French kingdom of Ys and Plato's lost isle of Atlantis. Myths? Perhaps. But the drowned Greek city of Helice exists, as do submerged Appolonia on the Libyan coast and Port Royal in Jamaica.

Built about 1655 by the English, Port Royal reached the apex of its notoriety as a base used by freebooter Henry Morgan when he sacked Spanish strongholds throughout the Caribbean. The buccaneer city, known as the wickedest in the world, flourished by trading in stolen goods and providing riotous diversions.

Toward noon on June 7, 1692, the earth heaved violently under Port Royal and the flimsy footings of the waterfront slid into the sea. Deep crevices rent the earth, devouring both buildings and panic-stricken

to the surface in wire cargo baskets suspended from plastic-coated cloth balloons. Often they rocketed jars upward by clearing them of sediment and filling them with air.

After divers had plotted and removed everything visible under the grids, only sand remained. They uncovered the next layer with an air lift that sometimes disgorged valuable small artifacts into a basket above. One of the most interesting objects was a ten-inch bronze bust of the goddess Athena—a lead-filled counterweight for a scale found earlier.

In 1962 the expedition set up headquarters on Yassi Island, building cagelike dormitories to keep out hundreds of rats overrunning the bleak rock. Though uncomfortable, this new camp eliminated the

people. Two-thirds of the city vanished, and 2,000 of its inhabitants died.

In 1959, Edwin A. Link, the aviation pioneer and industrialist who turned underwater explorer, sailed into the harbor of present-day Port Royal aboard his archeological research vessel, *Sea Diver.* His expedition, sponsored in part by the National Geographic Society, represented the first organized attempt to unreel the city's past. In the ten weeks allotted to the arduous task, the results were impressive. For one thing, Ed and Capt. P. V. H. Weems, retired naval officer and well-known navigator, drafted the first modern chart of pre-earthquake Port Royal.

With his divers, Ed retrieved hundreds of clues to life in 17th-century Jamaica. The most exciting find was a sea-blemished pocket watch. An X-ray photograph showed traces of the missing hands, pointing to 11:43, the exact time of the disaster.

Divers poked into the debris of a sunken cookhouse and amid a litter of kitchen utensils uncovered a battered copper pot containing cow and turtle bones clearly marked by a meat cleaver. Mixed with sooty brick fragments, the bones evoked a vision of the luncheon stew being buried as the chimney and the room collapsed.

Ed knew he had only begun. "It would take years of steady effort," he said, "to make a thorough search." And that search continues. In the past two years Robert F. Marx, a young archeologist from California, has uncovered thousands of clay pipes, a lode of pieces of eight, pewter, copperware—even a rum still.

One item in the sea's treasure chest excites the imagination more than any other

Crouched in the stern diving chamber of Sea Diver, *a ship equipped for underwater archeology and research, Edwin and Marion Link reach for a pewter plate and red roof tile brought up by divers returning from the ruins of Port Royal. The vessel works above the site of the old waterfront, defined by the area tinted light blue at far left. A brass pocket watch from the depths marked the moment of doom: X-rays of a limy encrustation from its face read 11:43.*

Hurricane shatters a homebound Spanish treasure fleet off the east coast of Florida, July 31, 1715

—gold. Walking the beach as a boy, I longed to find surf-tossed doubloons at my feet. I failed to realize this dream; others have succeeded.

The most spectacular treasure find of this century was encouraged by a friend of mine, Robert I. Nesmith, curator of the Foul Anchor Archives in Rye, New York, and one of America's foremost authorities on Spanish colonial coinage. I first met

him in 1956, and he introduced himself by saying, "Hi, I'm One-Dive Bob." Although frankly admitting to fragmentary underwater skills, he takes an avid interest in divers, especially those on the trail of gold.

"I'd like to tell you about an interesting man," Bob said, "a housebuilder from Florida, Kip Wagner, who spends every spare moment beachcombing. He showed me a perfect piece of eight turned over by

Waves swallowed $14,000,000 in gold and silver. Divers began work soon after, recovering half the loss.

his toe after a hurricane had shifted the sand at Sebastian Inlet north of Vero Beach. Then he found more by using a $15 military surplus mine detector. The coins were dated between 1649 and 1715 and many bore the stamp of the Mexico City mint. I told Kip they were the most important finds from a Spanish Plate Fleet ever made in Florida."

Bob was right. Kip Wagner found trea-sure worth well over a million dollars. Digging into history books, he learned that a hurricane in July, 1715, had destroyed a ten-ship Spanish treasure flotilla off Vero Beach. Reconnoitering the site in an air-plane, Kip spotted a dark patch in the shal-low water. Regular shapes projected from the shadowy form. Cannon? Returning next day in a skiff, he swam over the site wearing a diving mask and identified the patch as ballast stones, ringed by 18 encrusted cannon.

Next he bought a wallowing surplus Navy launch and recruited ten friends as a crew. The Real "8" Co., Inc., as they called themselves, set out for the wreck. Having obtained exclusive rights from Florida to excavate, they could keep 75 percent of all they salvaged.

The ship lay 20 feet down and 1,100 feet offshore in water swirling with seaweed and dark sand clouds. To remove the sand cover, they built an air lift. Soon they retrieved a set of bronze apothecary weights, several brass navigator's dividers, and some silver dishes. One momentous day a diver struggled to the surface bearing a 50-pound sea-blackened clump of pieces of eight. Others followed. Several exquisite bowls and cups of K'ang-hsi porcelain had survived because packers had protected them in the same kind of clay from which they had been made.

Beachcombing during bad weather, the men made their single most valuable find —a superbly crafted gold dragon hanging from an 11-foot gold chain of 2,176 intricate links. The dragon's mouth forms a whistle, a toothpick hinges into its belly, and its tail forms an ear-cleaning spoon.

When Kip auctioned the treasure early in 1967, I rooted for a secret bidder, Richard Dietrich. Dick and I had worked hard for months planning the new Underwater Museum in Philadelphia. Luckily, he won, and the beautiful dragon and several other pieces will go on exhibit there.

"When I look back on our struggles over the years," Kip wrote in 1965, "the money value of over a million dollars seems almost meaningless. The real treasure lies in our having touched hands with history.

"The excitement of the search, even the months of waiting and despair, have provided moments that could not be bought. Every find comes as a gift from the sea, and our best reward will always be the unforgettable thrill of discovery."

Certainly underwater explorers and archeologists the world over would shout a resounding "Amen!" to these eloquent words. I most certainly do.

Weathered steps of a treasure hunter's beach cabin hold a king's ransom in pieces of eight, gold ingots, chains, and doubloons, and delicate K'ang-hsi porcelain. In 1964 Floridian Kip Wagner launched a search that has recovered more than $1,000,000 in treasure from the ill-fated Spanish fleet. The gold doubloon below, actually about the size of a silver dollar, bears the name of King Philip V and the date 1714. At left, an elated diver surfaces with two of the gold coins.

NATIONAL GEOGRAPHIC PHOTOGRAPHERS BRUCE DALE (LEFT), AND ROBERT OAKES (BELOW); LUIS MARDEN, N.G.S. STAFF (OPPOSITE)

7

Taxis
to the Deep

BY JAMES DUGAN

Research submarine Aluminaut *cruises off Miami, Florida, during a test dive. Its lightweight aluminum hull resembles that of a conventional submarine but can withstand pressures ten times greater.*

THE AGITATED SEA CHURNED with frothy five-foot waves as Ed Link's *Sea Diver* struggled over the Bahamian horizon toward the pitching support vessel that had brought me to meet her. Fifty yards off our bow she dropped anchor. On her fantail I spotted *Deep Diver*, the bright-yellow, brand-new brainchild of Ed and submarine builder John H. Perry, Jr.

At Ed's invitation I would accompany the sturdy little vehicle on her eighteenth dive. He had set up sea trials for the submarino—my term for "submarine oceanographic," to distinguish the craft from military subs—off Grand Bahama Island, where the deep-blue, magically clear waters provided an excellent spot for the sprightly youngster's performances.

Deep Diver, unlike any other undersea research vessel now in operation, possesses a diver "lock-out" chamber, making her a true taxi to the deep, because divers can get in and out at will. Twenty-two feet long, the submarino contains two pressure compartments connected by a hatch. The forward chamber carries a pilot and observer; the one aft accommodates two divers. On bottom, the divers seal the connecting hatch and pressurize their chamber to match the outside water pressure.

They emerge through a downward-opening hatch and go about their work of sampling, salvage, or repair. Hoses from the sub feed them breathing-gas mixtures. The job done, they return to the vehicle's pressurized chamber and begin decompression on their way to the surface. Topside, *Deep Diver* couples with a deck chamber and the divers transfer to it, completing the process to avoid the bends. Thus *Deep Diver* is a submersible decompression chamber with mobility.

My voyage in this promising vessel took place on a spring morning in 1967 following a day-long 40-knot gale. Aboard *Sea Diver*, Ed's custom-tailored research ship, I watched the crew ready the little sub for launching in the disturbed sea. When lean, unflappable Mike Adams, the chief pilot, signaled it was time to go, I ducked under the open hatch and hoisted myself inside.

A crane held *Deep Diver* by a steel knuckle instead of a cable, eliminating dangerous swaying during launch operations. In the water, things changed. Submarinos are built to explore the world beneath the sea, not the surface. The swells tossed us around like dolls in a washing machine.

Mike released some air ballast, and we sank into the calm of the emerald underseascape. While military submarines are blind, except for an eye on a stalk that can rise above the surface, *Deep Diver* is all eyes. Twenty-one view ports leave her with few blind spots. Through a port at my feet I watched the bottom grow more distinct as we neared it. Coral heads dotted the placid scene, sea fans undulated in the current, and tropical fish swam past our windows.

We reached bottom at 60 feet. Designed to operate at 1,350 feet, *Deep Diver* moves slowly like all submarinos but can go up, down, forward, backward, and sideways. As we cruised along, an undersea village came into view. The "buildings" were Ed's Igloo and SPID (both submersible portable inflatable dwellings). During *Deep Diver*'s trials, aquanauts used her as a taxi to and from this sunken village and spent their bottom time performing such tasks as splicing a telephone cable.

Ed's submarino, like other taxis to the deep, resulted from the persistent efforts of men who refused to believe the sea floor need remain off limits to them. Only 40 years ago copper-helmeted William Beebe stood in 63 feet of water and looked over the edge of a steep precipice. "As I peered down I realized I was looking toward a world of life almost as unknown as that of Mars or Venus." he wrote in the NATIONAL GEOGRAPHIC. He realized, too, the folly of proceeding farther with nothing but a diving suit and helmet to protect him.

Beebe's frustrated curiosity led him to designer-engineer Otis Barton, and before long the first bathysphere was born. In 1934 this two-ton steel ball carried Beebe and Barton on an epic voyage 3,028 feet into a strange, mysterious realm.

As the bathysphere sank into the darkening water, Beebe experienced a kind of rapture of the deep. "I made my eyes focus in midwater and saw small creatures clearly, copepods and . . . innumerable swarms which haunt the upper layers." Passing the 1,000-foot mark, Beebe noted: "The last hint of blue tapers into a nameless gray, and this finally into black; but, from the present level down, the eye falters and the mind refuses any articulate color distinction. The sun is defeated, and color is banished forever, until a human at last penetrates and flashes a yellow electric ray into what has been jet black for two billion years."

From the bathysphere came the bathyscaph, the deep boat conceived by the brilliant engineer Auguste Piccard. I met the towering Swiss in Paris in the early 1950's when he was organizing his second bathyscaph campaign. His task would have daunted a lesser man—the development of an entirely new ballast system that would

WILLIAM BEEBE

Clambering over protruding door bolts, naturalist William Beebe squeezes from the steel bathysphere that in 1934 carried him and designer Otis Barton (in shorts) to a record 3,028 feet off Bermuda. From the three-inch-thick quartz window of the "lonely sphere," Beebe said, he "peered into the abysmal darkness . . . isolated as a lost planet in outermost space."

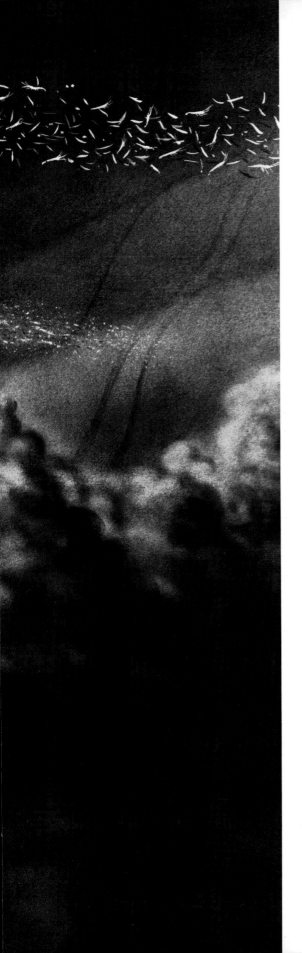

permit a vehicle to journey down into stupendous pressure, free of the surface tethers that had restricted the bathysphere.

Piccard attached a cabin to a huge gasoline-filled float with built-in silos containing iron pellets. At the touch of a button he could release either gasoline or pellets to descend, rise, or remain motionless. Thus he liberated the steel sphere to explore the deepest parts of the world ocean with only a telephone link to the surface.

Later, on January 23, 1960, Piccard's son Jacques and a young Navy lieutenant named Don Walsh took the bathyscaph *Trieste* on man's deepest dive, 35,800 feet into the Challenger Deep in the Mariana Trench. "Like a free balloon on a windless day, indifferent to the almost 200,000 tons of water pressing on the cabin from all sides . . . slowly, surely, in the name of science and humanity, the *Trieste* took possession of the abyss, the last extreme on our earth that remained to be conquered," Piccard wrote.

When he and Walsh landed seven miles down on the Pacific floor, they saw a small fish swimming nearby, the answer to an old riddle of the sea: Do fish live in the abyss?

"Our fish," said Piccard, "was the instantaneous reply . . . to a question that thousands of oceanographers had been asking themselves for decades. Slowly, very slowly, this fish—apparently of the sole family, about a foot long and half as wide—moved away from us, swimming half in the bottom ooze, and disappeared into the black night, the eternal night which was its domain." Taking a proud place in the succession of man's adventures in bathyscaphs, *Trieste* had plumbed the ultimate deep.

Mud clouds from an undersea avalanche billow around the bathyscaph F.N.R.S. 3 *in Toulon Canyon, off southern France. During more than an hour of immobility—before the craft began rising slowly to the surface—the crew feared deep mire had buried them 5,250 feet down. The bathyscaph, carrying Captain Cousteau and Lt. Comdr. Georges S. Houot of the French Navy, touched off the slide after settling on a ledge while exploring the canyon in 1954.*

PAINTING BY ROLF KLEP

Lashed by waves that tore loose a towline, the bathyscaph Trieste *undergoes repairs before its 35,800-foot descent in 1960 into the Mariana Trench — earth's deepest known chasm. Minutes later,*

Jacques Piccard (right) and U. S. Navy Lt. Don Walsh climbed inside the craft and ventured down nearly seven miles. They touched bottom near a slow-moving fish, proving life exists in the abyss.

In the summer of 1954, Captain Cousteau waited with Lt. Comdr. Georges S. Houot, master of the French Navy bathyscaph *F.N.R.S. 3,* while the fickle Mediterranean weather forced repeated postponements of a dive in the open sea. Finally, overcome with impatience, Cousteau and Houot squeezed into the bathyscaph's cramped sphere with a briefcase of sandwiches and wine. They went down in a coastal submarine canyon near Toulon, France, and began one of the strangest and most exciting voyages the little boat ever made.

"At last the bathyscaph sank into green silence," Cousteau recalled for me. "A little deeper, the water shaded into blue. At 1,000 feet it was practically dark. In the light of the exterior droplights I saw crazy 'snow' falling upward. The flakes were tiny suspended organisms passing as we fell; otherwise, there was no sensation of motion in the bathyscaph.

"At 4,600 feet I asked Houot to slow the descent. He reduced our falling speed to ten inches a second. A few moments later he looked at the echo-sound graph.

"'According to this,' he said, 'the bottom's about 200 feet below us.'

Stripped of its outer shell, the diving saucer gets a cleaning and checkup on Calypso's *deck. Power assemblies lie between inner and outer hulls, so the crew faces minimum danger from fires or noxious gases caused by motors or damaged batteries. The hydraulic claw extended above the viewing ports picks up samples from the continental shelves. At right, the saucer hovers for a portrait in the Mediterranean Sea.*

"As he spoke, I saw beyond the droplights, perhaps as far away as the bow, a vague, cloudy shape. 'Listen, that's the bottom over there. We're down already.'

"'Absurd,' said Houot.

"'If that isn't the bottom, what is it?' I asked him.

"'What's going on, anyway?' said Houot. 'The depth gauge, the sonic detector, and the vertical speed indicator all say we're still going down.'

"The depth gauge read 4,920 feet. I was astonished to see that our craft was standing on an undulating shelf of mud right at the edge of a vertical cliff. The cloud we had seen was a cliff rising sheer above us. And yet, a chart compiled by echo soundings from surface vessels showed the walls

Author James Dugan, photographed only weeks before his death on June 1, 1967, emerges from the submarino Deep Diver *after a descent in the Bahamas. Another hatch underneath permits divers in a "lock-out" chamber to come and go as they please. At right,* Deep Diver *awaits launching from the deck of Ed Link's* Sea Diver.

of the canyon to have a regular slope of 20 to 30 degrees. The actual crevasse, as we could now see, was carved into large steps. Obviously, the echo sounder was not a sufficiently discriminating instrument for bathyscaph work.

" 'Shall we start the motors and drive off the cliff?' I asked. Houot pressed the shot-release button for 20 seconds. Slowly the bathyscaph rose about five feet; some of the guide chain remained coiled in the mud. Houot ran both motors ahead. *F.N.R.S. 3* started sluggishly, apparently held back by the chain. Then she pulled free—and things began to happen. I saw a great block of hard mud tumble off the ledge, dislodging more big lumps. Clouds bloomed below, boiled up, and spread.

" 'Houot, we've started an avalanche!'

"For 20 minutes we waited, looking down into thick clouds that would not subside. We thought we might find clear bottom by steering across the canyon on a compass bearing, even though it would mean sailing directly through the disturbance. It was a mad crossing. The width of the canyon is about 1,300 feet, and we had been under way for twenty minutes, ample time at our one-knot speed to reach the other wall. Our motors were running, but suddenly we became aware of a chilling fact: particles no longer rushed at our window. We were not moving.

"Could we have loosened the opposite canyon wall and now be buried deep in soft mud? At the portholes, only opaque yellow. It is strange to sit in a blind steel ball 5,250 feet down reflecting on the fact that canyons which suddenly acquire huge shelves

may also have large overhangs capable of trapping a little submarine that always wants to go up.

"An hour passed, and the water still had not cleared. We decided to surface. Even though Houot jettisoned a lot of shot, the depth gauge and the vertical-speed indicator did not move. Our theory of an overhang gained considerable substance. Things cannot be this bad, I thought. Had we forgotten something?

"And then it came to us: in the hour we had waited here in the cold, the gasoline must have cooled even further. Unquestionably, we had grown really heavy. Houot squirted more shot from the silos. We heard it hailing down on our sphere. A moment

passed, and suddenly the speed indicator stirred. I saw specks sliding down the window. We were climbing! Daylight came faintly at last and swelled into a green haze.

"Back ashore, I told Professor Jacques Bourcart, 'You know that canyon you charted so carefully? You'll have to do it again. We just wrecked it.'"

The bathysphere and bathyscaph were built to carry man into the extreme depths of the abyss, but it took a submarine tragedy and a lost nuclear bomb to bring into focus the great potential of submarinos.

On April 10, 1963, the U.S.S. *Thresher*—then the most advanced nuclear attack submarine ever built—put to sea on a voyage that cost the life of the boat and her 129-

man crew, a disaster unparalleled in underwater history. *Thresher* collapsed and went down in 8,490 feet of water off the coast of New England. The intensive and frustrating search for the wreck emphasized the lack of useful experience in exploring the vast undersea world.

Finding *Thresher* was like finding a tin can in ten square miles of uncharted jungle. Efforts to locate the wreck underscored the need for highly mobile underwater vehicles with great endurance, and for deep-sea rescue vessels to aid stricken submarines. At that time the bathyscaph *Trieste* was the Navy's only craft capable of reaching *Thresher*'s grave. The deep boat recovered pieces of the wreckage after cameras lowered from surface vessels had pinpointed the site. But *Trieste* functions as little more than an elevator, and is almost completely helpless in a situation calling for wide horizontal searching range.

Three years later, in January, 1966, a U. S. B-52 rendezvoused with a flying tanker for routine refueling six miles above Palomares, Spain. Suddenly the tanker exploded in a burst of flame that sent the B-52 plunging in a fiery shower of men and machinery. In that fiery shower were four H-bombs.

Three of them fell on land, but the fourth dropped into the sea and sank 2,550 feet to the dark and hidden floor below. Though unarmed, the powerful nuclear weapon had to be recovered. The U. S. Navy hurriedly sent a task force of research vessels, divers, and submersibles to the Spanish coastal waters off Palomares. In the end, the submarinos *Alvin* and *Aluminaut* provided the key to the suspenseful search.

Operated by the Woods Hole Oceanographic Institution for the Office of Naval Research, *Alvin* has a depth capacity of

Silvery bubbles escape from a night diver's breathing gear as he exits from the lock-out chamber of Deep Diver. *Another compartment inside the submersible holds the pilot and an observer. Propellers fore and aft enable the craft to turn 360° within its own length of 22 feet.*
JERRY GREENBERG

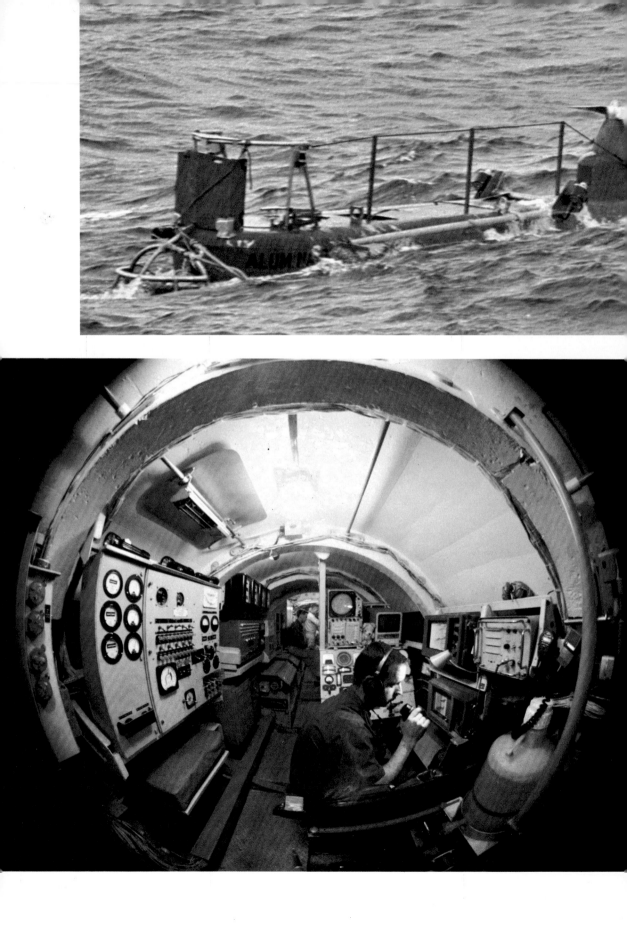

Deepwater submarino, Aluminaut *surfaces in choppy seas off Miami. The craft, designed to descend 15,000 feet—far enough to study more than 60 percent of the ocean floor—can carry three crewmen and three observers. The propeller amidships permits vertical maneuvering. Fisheye-* *lens reveals the interior, where banks of equipment measure currents, temperature, and salinity. Sonar continuously charts the ocean floor. Both* Aluminaut *and* Alvin *(below) helped recover the H-bomb that in 1966 fell from a burning B-52 into the sea near Palomares, Spain.*

Mechanical hand extends from Alvin's bow, ready to pluck objects at depths of 6,000 feet and hold them before the viewing port for inspection. *Three crewmen operate from a pressure-resistant steel sphere inside. Litton Industries built the sub for Woods Hole Oceanographic Institution.*

6,000 feet. Reynolds International's *Alumi-naut*, the first forged-aluminum submarine, can submerge to 15,000 feet. Their locating the bomb—and its eventual recovery after eleven weeks—demonstrated the importance of advanced underwater engineering. The emergency need for submarinos so painfully revealed by *Thresher* and the lost bomb also stimulated U. S. industrialists to pour more money and effort into developing underwater vehicles.

Cousteau had anticipated the potential of the submarino in 1959 when he built the now famous diving saucer. This compact little craft literally flies the ocean depths down to 1,100 feet, and has carried scores of scientists on exploratory excursions.

Until undersea research vessels came along, a scientist could study the ocean world only from surface vessels, fairly shallow dives, or relatively brief descents to one spot. Now he can see that world for himself. He can go deep, stay long, and do work that will unlock secrets shrouded for millions of years.

In the early 1930's Francis Parker Shepard, a pioneer marine geologist, staked out the Scripps Submarine Canyon off southern California for intensive study. For years he groped for the canyon's form, first with sounding lines dangled from a rowboat, then with sonar, a robot depth camera, and divers. In 1964 Shepard took a trip into his elusive canyon in Cousteau's diving saucer. After wandering euphorically among the mysteries so long hidden from him, Shepard emerged triumphantly and summed up his experience: "In three hours I learned more about the canyon than I have in the last three years."

Soon students will share the experiences of underwater scientists. At Florida Atlantic University a Perry Cubmarine, a small submarino, will ferry students to and from an undersea classroom in 40 feet of water off Palm Beach. The craft will lock into an entry chamber beneath the laboratory.

Ocean Systems, Inc., partly owned by Ed Link, operates a small fleet of Cubmarines with depth ranges from 150 to 1,350 feet. *Deep Diver*, in fact, belongs to the Cubmarine

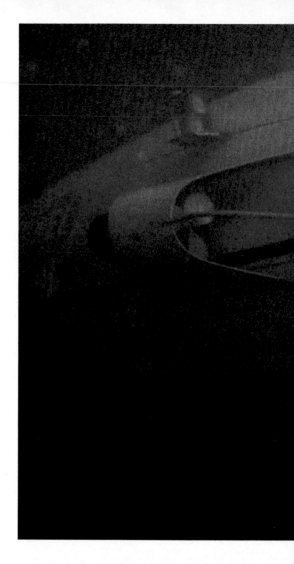

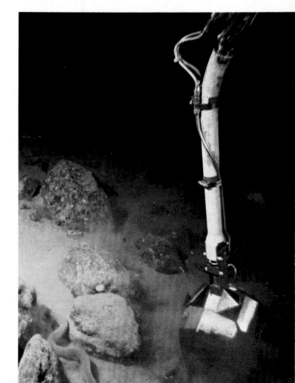

Versatile and maneuverable, Deepstar-4000 roams the continental slope near the California coast. The 4000 indicates the working depth of the diving vehicle, patterned after Cousteau's earlier, smaller version. The three-man crew— usually a pilot and two scientist-observers— squeeze into a spherical pressure chamber inside the 18-foot-long hull. They communicate by telephone with surface vessels or other submersibles within a range of 7,500 yards. Lead-acid batteries supply propulsion for 8-hour missions,

and reversible propellers provide thrust and mobility. A cluster of lights at the nose, for 70mm still and 16mm movie photography, illuminates a world dark since time began. The craft's hydraulically operated claw (opposite) gathers floor samples and deposits them in a collecting basket attached to the hull. An eel-like hagfish slithers out of the way. Brittle stars, numerous at 4,000 feet, pattern the bottom beside a deep-water sculpin (lower left) and a rarely seen deep-sea skate (right). Burrowing worms texture the mud.

family. In 1966 these versatile submarinos scurried below to test and to survey transatlantic telephone cables.

Countless chores await these and other diving taxis, and the tasks will grow as equipment for undersea research vessels becomes increasingly sophisticated. The sea gives up its secrets reluctantly. Still, in a relatively short time submarinos have achieved a fascinating, impressive record.

Edwin C. Buffington, a geological oceanographer from the U. S. Naval Electronics Laboratory Center, let me listen to his tape-recorded log of a *Deepstar-4,000* dive off southern California. Built by Cousteau for Westinghouse, *Deepstar* evolved from the diving saucer. Ed Buffington's log gave me new insight into how adventurous investigators put submarinos to use:

"1218. We have begun our descent.... We are in a slight stern-down attitude as we make our descent and rotate counterclockwise rather rapidly. It is a murky day ... we don't have much light penetration.... I see a few jellyfish and Salp chains....

"1223. Depth 20 fathoms above the bottom. The descent weight has been dropped and we ... assume a nose-down attitude.

"1226. We have settled on the bottom....

"1227. ... we are exactly 75 fathoms below the surface. There is very little wildlife down here. I see a sea pen, an orange star fish.... The slope is exceedingly smooth — no corrugations, ripples, and an almost complete absence of animal burrows and mounds.... We are stopping here briefly ... to get our gyro compass set up, ... also ... to take a core.

"1240. We are repositioning the *Deepstar* to point upslope.... the coring technique will be to grasp the head of the core in the claw and position it vertically in front of *Deepstar;* then tilt the *Deepstar* forward.... the core penetrated about 4 inches but in sliding backward down the slope dragged it out obliquely. We have approximately an inch and a half of sample.... This is not bad; we have learned something from this.

"1401. Depth 181 fathoms.... The bottom here has almost a silky texture.... There are some animal tracks and ... large

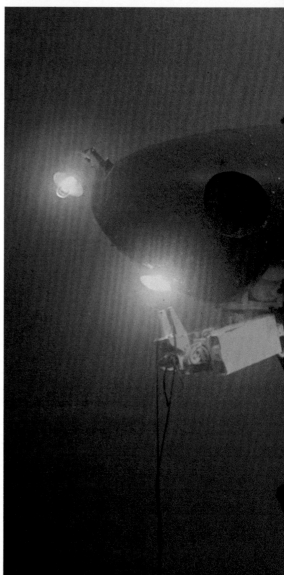

numbers of little hermit crabs. . . . The water is now full of these beautiful little red Euphausiid shrimps. . . . The critter population has increased tremendously. . . .

"1410. Depth 208 fathoms. . . . we have stopped where we see a large rock outcrop. . . . looks like a porphyritic basalt.

"1414. . . . We are on a 25-degree slope which is strewn with large boulders. . . . We came to a rather abrupt halt. . . . seems like

Flippered divers make last-minute equipment checks on Star III *before the start of an underwater mapping mission 600 feet down off Key West. Two 35mm cameras mounted under the bow take stereophotographs of the ocean bottom. At left, crewmen secure lines to the support ship.*

Deepstar got its shoelaces caught on a rock. . . . It's amazing how some of these rocks are not covered with any material at all. . . . Dead ahead . . . real large outcrop or boulder . . . we're just floating over the top of it —we won't touch it—I hope.

"1445. . . . Now we are sliding sideways again and have come to the edge of an almost completely vertical dropoff. . . . We are going off the edge. It looks like El Capitan. . . . It's beautiful, beautiful, beautiful!!!

"1601. Depth 301 fathoms. . . . Just saw a large flat fish—a halibut maybe, a couple of feet long. There are many artifacts, chunks of cable, cardboard cartons, etc.

"1608. Depth 310 fathoms. We are terminating our dive. . . ."

Unfortunately the sea offers implacable

resistance to the invasion of submarinos. Awesomely deep, dark, and cold, it is a gigantic space through which these tiny vessels can move only at low speed. Life-support systems for the crew take up space and increase the weight. The larger the vehicle, the more power it requires to push it through the viscous sea. To double submerged speed, a propulsion system must deliver *eight* times more power. Today submarinos run on various kinds of batteries, but each type has serious limitations.

THE EPISODE from *Deepstar's* log reveals another challenge confronting submarino builders—precision control. Future undersea research vehicles will require more stability and dexterity. They must, in effect, be able to serve man as deftly as his own hands in performing intricate work at great depths.

To make design problems even more complex, each undersea voyage requires the submarino to display different capabilities. A geologist will want it to carry one set of tools, the marine biologist another. The physical oceanographer will have still other needs. Designers are making progress in coping with these demands.

For example, Jacques Piccard has teamed with the Grumman Aircraft Company to build a specialized submarino, the PX-15, in which he hopes to carry out an unprecedented mission. With a crew of scientists he will submerge in the Gulf Stream off the Florida coast and drift with the four-knot current to a point off Halifax, Nova Scotia —a distance of 1,450 nautical miles.

At depths varying from 300 to 2,000 feet, the PX-15 will remain submerged for four to six weeks. At intervals, technicians will check the temperature of the water, its salinity, and its chemical composition to determine the effect on undersea life observed along the way.

The craft will become the first silent undersea observation post for prolonged use. Scientists will peer out 29 portholes, using specially designed lighting equipment, and what they see may eclipse the wildest lore of the past. They will enjoy hot

meals and will have warm, fresh water for bathing. The PX-15 may well usher in a new era of manned undersea vehicles.

In less than ten years the submarinos have grown from Cousteau's little saucer to a small fleet of some 25 craft exploring the world ocean. The third of General Dynamics' *Star* series, built to operate at 2,000 feet, has made stereophotographic maps of a section of the continental shelf. Lockheed's new *Deep Quest* can carry 7,000 pounds—including crew and instruments —to a depth of 8,000 feet and also double as a submarine rescue vehicle.

The Navy's Deep Submergence Systems Project has accelerated its development of undersea vehicles for rescue, salvage, and exploration of the continental shelf. Engineers already are designing a deep-search sub that can descend 20,000 feet. In 1968 the Navy will launch a rescue vessel capable of coupling with a distressed submarine and removing its entire crew on successive dives. Later in the year, the Navy also hopes to complete the NR-1, the first nuclear-powered deep-sea research vehicle. If successful, the NR-1 will be free to cruise the ocean bottom for weeks at a time.

In spite of all man's efforts and his mushrooming technology, the sea remains a great riddle, as it was a thousand, even a hundred years ago. Far from having most of the answers, man has yet to discover some of the questions.

The submarinos and those who build and use them will be a growing part of the search. The thirst for knowledge which drives men forward will, perhaps, ultimately prevail over the hostility of the sea. Regardless of the cost, the dangers, and the bristling array of obstacles the sea throws up to guard her ancient secrets, we are, as masters of our planet, determined to conquer its final frontier.

Coppery Caribbean sunset silhouettes the French bathyscaph Archimède, *under tow near its diving site over the Puerto Rico Trench in 1964. Named for the Greek philosopher who discovered the principle of buoyancy,* Archimède *can explore the sea's greatest depths.*

8

Harvests of the Future

BY RICHARD M. CRUM

Surging waters yield a bounty of abalone to Japanese diving women, the ama, *whose occupation goes back 1,500 years. Today, scientists find the sea a rich source of fuels and minerals as well as food.*

"FLOUR FROM THE SEA can enrich a limitless variety of foods," Mrs. Virginia Sidwell said, her eyes sparkling as she handed me a chocolate-chip cookie. She had made it with Fish Protein Concentrate (FPC)—a flour produced by grinding up raw fish: heads, fins, bones, and all.

Cautiously, I chewed the cookie. Surprised, I discovered no fish taste. The cookie, in fact, was delicious.

"FPC is odorless and so bland it's almost tasteless," Mrs. Sidwell said proudly. A nutritionist, she prepares recipes for foods fortified with FPC for the Technological Laboratory of the U.S. Bureau of Commercial Fisheries in Washington, D.C.

Researchers at the laboratory, under the direction of chemist Donald G. Snyder, have developed the first approved commercial process for manufacturing FPC in the United States. By the end of this decade, a large-scale plant is scheduled to begin operation in the Pacific Northwest. Other countries developing FPC factories include Sweden, Canada, the Republic of South Africa, and the U.S.S.R.

Dr. Snyder enthusiastically explained the potential of fish flour to me. "Since FPC is 80 percent animal protein, we can mix it with grain flours and get a product with a higher food value. This way, the concentrate provides one answer to the world's need for high-quality protein at low cost. By using the whole fish we keep the price down so the poor of all nations, the people who need such nutrition the most, can afford it.

"FPC won't feed all the people in the world, but combined with other sources of protein such as peas, soybeans, and cottonseed meal, it will make deep inroads into the problem of hunger. Less than half a cent's worth mixed in the diet can fulfill a child's daily minimum protein needs."

Throughout the world today two billion people do not have enough to eat. Hunger kills millions of children before they reach age five. Those who survive often face a shortened life or mental retardation because their diet fails to supply the essential amino acids found in protein.

To help curb increasing hunger, man

looks more and more toward the sea. Up to now, this vast food locker has barely been touched. More than four-fifths of earth's animals live in the sea. Yet of some 20,000 species of ocean fish, man hunts only a few dozen. Some marine biologists believe that 250 million tons, five times the present world catch, could be landed each year by going after such underfished species as mackerel and hake.

Although the sea's food is abundant, it is not inexhaustible. Already man hunts most commercial fish to capacity. As modern fishing craft become more efficient, biologists put stronger stress on conservation.

To preserve marine wildlife and to reap a more plentiful harvest, man may stop hunting fish and start farming them. Marine husbandry, called aquiculture, resembles the animal husbandry practiced on land. Sea farmers corral their charges, control their growth by doling out food, and protect them from larger fish.

No system of agriculture today matches the marine farm for producing high-calorie food. An acre of prime shellfish ground, for example, can supply 15,000 pounds of protein yearly.

Sedentary creatures, such as shellfish that stay fixed in one place and don't need fencing, prove the most practical sea animals to farm today.

Italy's Taranto Bay produces an incredible 108,000 pounds of mussels per acre each year. The world's greatest single source of oysters is Chesapeake Bay. Sown regularly with seed oysters, it yields some 20 million pounds of the shellfish each year.

For a century, oyster-raising has been an industry in the United States. But spawning the bivalves artifically in privately owned nurseries is new. Only five commercial oyster hatcheries exist in the world.

Eager to see one, I visited Sayville, Long

THE AUTHOR: *Richard M. Crum traveled to the Pacific, Atlantic, and Gulf coasts, gathering information for "Harvests of the Future." A freelance writer in landlocked Oklahoma, Mr. Crum joined the U. S. Navy in 1958 and served as a navy journalist. Since 1964, he has been on the staff of the National Geographic Society.*

NATIONAL GEOGRAPHIC PHOTOGRAPHER BATES W. LITTLEHALES

Polynesian diver and his wife probe lagoons in the Tuamotu Archipelago for black-lipped pearl shells. Despite his bulk, he moves in water with grace and speed. Buyers prize the lustrous shell (below) for knife handles, earrings, and buttons. Cheeks squeezed by pressure, a diver off Takaroa atoll plucks a lime-encrusted mother-of-pearl oyster in a bed of staghorn coral 20 fathoms down.

In cool waters off California, swaying blades
of giant kelp reach toward the light. Buoyed by
gas bladders (opposite, below), kelp fronds may
grow two feet a day, and stretch more than 200
feet to form a tangled canopy at the surface. In
this dim jungle fishes shelter and sea urchins
graze. Commercial mowing barges reap the kelp
like hay. Largest of all marine plants, it yields
algin, used in products as diverse as toothpaste,
paints, drugs, gumdrops, and fertilizer.

ROBERT AMES; OPPOSITE, TOP TO BOTTOM:
ROGER COAR, NATE LAWRENCE, EDWARD ZIMBELMAN

A biologist collects giant kelp, seeking a strain for seabeds where high temperatures have killed less-resistant types.

Sea otter, the major predator of kelp-destroying sea urchins, cradles in a leafy raft near Point Lobos, California.

Shallow rearing pools of a pioneer shrimp ranch
nurture delicacies by the millions beside Japan's
Inland Sea. The owner (below) holds a female

ready to spawn. Her young will spend their first
three weeks in tile-lined temperature-controlled
hatchery tanks before being moved to the ponds.

Island. With Mrs. David Wallace, Director of the Oyster Institute of North America, I toured Shellfish, Inc., a nursery that fronts Great South Bay, home of the nationally famous bluepoint oyster.

Mr. Charles Hart, owner of Shellfish, Inc., greeted us and ushered us through a white door marked "Maternity Ward." Inside, stacked trays held shale-colored oysters being cooled in bubbling water.

"These are my parent stock," Mr. Hart said, "oysters ripe for spawning. We keep them in water cooled below 60° F. By placing a few dozen in a separate tank and raising the water temperature to 72° F. we

cause them to spawn. We siphon off the eggs and fertilize them by adding sperm to the water. Within six hours millions of tiny larvae hatch and swim around."

Looking into a microscope, I watched dozens of transparent shelled larvae bounce about in a molluscan discothèque.

"By controlling the growth of the young oysters we can protect them from predators and increase our harvest," Mr. Hart said. "When the spat reach thumbnail size, about eight weeks old, they can fend for themselves and we plant them on the bay bottom. It's just like sowing grain.

"Our oysters are bred and farmed to be

171

With hypodermic needles, Florida biologists inject shrimp with green dye. Released in the sea, marked crustaceans help trace their migration patterns when caught in trawls like the one at right.

eaten on the half-shell. They have to be farmed in order to get premium flavor and also to produce a round shell that looks good on the plate. Planting them on hard bottom and giving them plenty of room lets the shell grow round instead of long. In three full summers they reach maturity, and we harvest them for market. We expect to gather 2,000 bushels of oysters this year. They'll sell for about $25 a bushel."

Japan leads all other nations in aquiculture. Seafood farmers grow oysters on long ropes dangling from rafts in waveless inlets. As the spat cling at intervals to the ropes, they feed on plankton that drift slowly past—and they grow faster and fatter than they would on the bottom. From these perpendicular "pastures" come 32,000 pounds of oysters per acre of water.

That most famous of all aquiculture products, the cultured pearl, is produced on some 300 farms in the protected bays and inlets of southern Japan. Exports of such pearls bring the country more than $50,000,000 a year.

Aquiculturists in Okachi Bay, 200 miles northeast of Tokyo, farm salmon and trout. Caged in nylon nets 65 feet below the surface, the fish fatten on enriched food pellets and chopped raw sardines.

The coral atolls of the Pacific may provide acreage for future fish farms. These island chains ring shallow lagoons hundreds of square miles in area. Professor John D. Isaacs, of the Scripps Institution of Oceanography, told me the enclosed waters form natural sites for curbing and controlling large populations of fish. Deposits of phosphate in the atolls may furnish a natural source of fertilizer for enriching the lagoons. Also, atomic power plants, by discharging heated water, could create upwellings of nutrients needed for fertility.

Dr. Milner B. Schaefer, former Director

PETER DAVID, PHOTO RESEARCHERS, INC. (UPPER LEFT); NATIONAL GEOGRAPHIC PHOTOGRAPHER BATES W. LITTLEHALES (LEFT); AND JERRY GREENBERG

King of seafood in the U. S., tiny shrimp surpass salmon and tuna in commercial value. A diver snares a spiny lobster, and a conservation officer destroys a lobster trap left by poachers.

of the Institute of Marine Resources at Scripps, explained a method of cultivating the unbridled herds of the ocean. "In the vast reaches of the open sea, aquiculture is not likely to prove feasible for a very long time. However, it is perfectly possible to *manage* the fisheries of the open sea by selective harvesting. We can encourage maximum production of the kinds of fish we want by suppressing predators, just as in range management we suppress wolves to increase cattle production."

Aquiculture includes the cultivation of marine plants as well as animals. Japan harvests nearly two dozen edible seaweeds. In the United States seaweed crops yield algin and carrageenin, used in chocolate milk, jellies, jams, cosmetics, and drugs.

No species of sea plant in the Northern Hemisphere rivals the giant kelp that grows along the coast from Alaska to Baja California, looming in awesome forests in its south-

ern range. I vividly remember exploring one underwater glen as a youngster. Descending in a diving bell off Santa Catalina Island, I marveled at seemingly endless streamers of kelp winnowing in the currents. The majestic columns of yellowish-green fronds stretched from the rocky bottom to surface sunlight 50 feet away.

Giant kelp—the fastest growing plant known—shoots upward to lengths of more than 200 feet. During World War I, it became a major source of potash in the United States. Today it is gathered, pulverized, and mixed with cattle feed as a protein supplement. Because kelp contains more concentrated minerals and proteins than most plants, it could become an important source of nutrition for man.

In addition to plants and animals, the sea holds almost every known element, including an estimated 10 million tons of gold, 500 million tons of silver, and 20 billion

173

tons of uranium. But this vast hoard lies out of man's reach today, scattered through earth's 300 million cubic miles of seawater.

My curiosity about the vast treasures hoarded by the sea led me to San Diego for a visit with Dr. John L. Mero, president of Ocean Resources, Inc., one of the companies pioneering in ocean mining.

"Offshore mining is at the same stage that mining on land was 300 years ago," Dr. Mero told me. "Mineral deposits litter the sea floor, waiting to be picked up."

He handed me a blue-black rock shaped like a potato. "That's a manganese nodule. About 1.5 trillion tons of these nodules clutter the floor of the Pacific Ocean alone. They contain not only manganese but also copper, cobalt, nickel, molybdenum, and many other metals.

"In the next five to ten years we will see hundreds of near-shore placer deposits mined: gold, platinum, diamonds, and other heavy minerals," he said, showing me a small plastic vial of gold shavings taken from the drowned sands of the Seward Peninsula of Alaska. The sands are an extension of the Nome Gold Coast, an area that yielded $100,000,000 in the early 1900's. Besides precious yellow nuggets, pay streaks of platinum may line the subsea river valleys off Alaska.

I asked about diamonds.

"Dredges have brought up more than $500,000 worth of diamonds in a single month off the mouth of the Orange River in South-West Africa," Dr. Mero answered. "The whole southwest coast of Africa is a potential diamond field as far offshore as 80 miles. But mining them is expensive and hazardous—no harbors, rough waters, fog, desolate coast, no communications. The dangers and the lack of technology have slowed the development of ocean mining. But I think that within the next 30 years

Underwater "cowhands" ride the range on a fish ranch of the future. The central shaft leads to a supply ship, permitting emergency access to the surface. Sea-floor pipelines carry air to form bubble "fences." Scientists envision such villages, where men can live for long periods in the sea.

offshore mining will be a five- to ten-billion-dollar industry."

Already, offshore tin mines enrich Malaysia, Thailand, and Indonesia. The Japanese have dredged seven million tons of iron ore from the bottom of Tokyo Bay.

I examined a jagged tooth of rock on Dr. Mero's desk. "Phosphorite," he said. "Good for making fertilizers. It has been found off Peru, Chile, Mexico, South Africa, and Japan. Just off the coast of California there is probably a 200-year reserve of phosphorite nodules." He also mentioned that 20 million tons of oyster shells a year are scooped from the U. S. continental shelf for lime, poultry grit, and cement.

THE MOST common mineral is sodium chloride—table salt. Each cubic mile of seawater contains 121 million tons of salt worth about $1.2 billion. Seawater supplies most of the world's bromine, used in gasoline production. The bulk of the world's magnesium, the lightest structural metal known, comes from the sea, too.

"By the year 2000," Dr. Mero said, "offshore wells probably will supply 50 percent of the world's oil. Already 16 percent of all our oil flows from beneath the sea."

Petroleum companies surpass all other industries in exploiting the subsea floor. Giant corporate prospectors of black gold spend $2,000,000 a day keeping offshore rigs drilling. Oilmen believe the sea hides one trillion barrels of petroleum, three times as much as man has tapped since the beginning of history.

A forest of derricks rises from continental-shelf fields around the world. In the United States, drillers in the Gulf of Mexico lead the sea hunt for oil. At least 2.2 billion barrels lie below the Gulf.

At the Shell Oil Company offices in New Orleans, I called on a pioneer in offshore drilling, Mr. John W. Pittman. "Oil companies probably use more divers than any other marine industry," he said. "We literally waded into the field by tracking oil deposits from the land to the marshes and finally out into the Gulf. We completed the first well in the Gulf in the late 1930's,

Tomorrow: roundup time in the sea. Teams of porpoises, at electronic command from ranchers in submersibles, drive plump fish from a bubble corral to the harvesting area. There suction hoses will draw the fish into ships for cleaning and freezing. Divers control the gate with air valves.

but only in the last ten years has offshore drilling reached a fever pitch."

Mr. Pittman led me into a conference room and pointed to a wall map of the Gulf checkered with colored squares. "Each square represents 5,000-acre blocks leased by different companies. There are more than four million acres under lease by the industry. In terms of expenditures, the East Texas boom of the 30's was just a drop in the bucket compared to the Gulf. Each offshore rig may cost us up to $15,000 a day to operate. There are about 4,600 wells in the Gulf producing more than 700,000 barrels of oil a day."

To learn how oceangoing oilmen operate, I boarded a twin-engine seaplane with Fines Martin, a top Shell engineer. We crossed the Mississippi River and, near Morgan City, Louisiana, circled a bustling shipyard near the Intracoastal Waterway. Below, I saw a latticework of steel pipes forming a huge A-shaped outline.

"That will be one side of Platform 'A'," Fines said. "When completed, it will be the tallest offshore permanent platform in the world, taller than the Statue of Liberty. The platform will stand on the bottom in 340 feet of water, anchored by pilings driven 300 feet into the sea floor. Twelve to 24 offshore wells can be drilled from each Shell platform."

We banked away from Morgan City and sailed beyond the marshy shore near Grand Isle. Suddenly I spotted three long, narrow, bridgelike sections joined to form a Y-shaped platform in the water. "The world's first offshore sulphur mine," Fines said. "Another resource of the sea."

Like a large seabird, our plane swooped down and landed on the water at Southwest Pass, a branch at the mouth of the Mississippi River. Here a submarine net-

work of pipelines funnels more than 90,000 barrels of oil a day from offshore wells to nearby processing tanks.

Climbing into a helicopter, Fines and I hopped back out over the Gulf. The surface changed from silty brown to pale blue as the water deepened. Twenty minutes out, we sighted *Ocean Explorer*, one of the most modern seagoing rigs afloat. As tall as a

PAINTED FOR N.G.S. BY RICHARD SCHLECHT

22-story building, the mammoth V-shaped vessel straddled the waves on 20 bottle-shaped legs. A derrick tapered skyward from this bizarre ship, a wildcat rig probing for oil 50 miles from land.

After we eased down on *Ocean Explorer's* heliport, I followed Fines down a catwalk to the main deck. *Explorer* carries a crew of 43 men who enjoy air conditioned living quarters, a recreation room, and workshops.

"The rig can drill in waters as deep as 600 feet," Fines said. Tugs tow the ungainly structure to the drilling site, where it is secured by nine 11-ton anchors. To provide surface stability, crewmen flood 24 huge ballast tanks, sinking the platform's legs 70 feet. Crewmen can work undisturbed in seas running as high as 20 feet.

At times, during storms, the seas run higher. Hurricanes are nature's worst threat to the offshore drilling fleet. In 1964 hurricane Hilda slapped the oil industry with damages totaling $20,000,000. One crewman I met braved the wrath of Hilda in the giant rig, *Ocean Driller*. "Fifty-foot waves crashed over the main deck," he said. "Winds jerked our anchors loose and blew us 30 miles down the Gulf."

The potential of the sea to spawn storms reveals another of its resources — power. Today the French harness tides to produce electricity. In the Rance River estuary near St. Malo in Brittany the ebb and flow of powerful 40-foot tides spin turbines producing thousands of kilowatts.

BUT OF ALL THE SEA'S RESOURCES, the most priceless is fresh water. More than 100 million gallons flow daily from desalination plants throughout the world.

Key West, Florida, with 34,000 people, fills all its water needs from the sea, the first U. S. city to do so. A desalination plant supplies residents of this coral island with more than two million gallons of water daily.

By the early 1970's the world's first nuclear desalination plant will rise from a man-made island off Bolsa Chica State Beach in arid southern California. The plant will produce 150 million gallons of fresh water a day — enough for 750,000 persons. Its nuclear reactors will generate electric power for two million people.

Unfortunately, mankind's ledger of marine assets contains a serious debit entry — pollution. Already coastal waters show serious effects of being used as a dumping ground. In the past, near-shore waters served well as garbage disposals. But today a burgeoning population is swamping the sea with waste.

In the United States some 52 million people, one-fourth of the population, live within 50 miles of the seacoasts. From these congested areas a torrent of domestic and industrial effluents spills directly into bays, estuaries, and coastal waters. At times the discharge of waste overflows the sea's capacity for diluting it, and pollution results.

Such poisoning of near-shore waters not only threatens sea life but also endangers one of man's most cherished marine resources — recreation. Confined in an increasingly urban environment, restless millions turn to the sea as an outlet for the adventurous spirit.

"Every benefit we hope to derive from the ocean, including recreation, demands that we put scientific knowledge to practical use," said Robert Abel, director of a new concept in ocean study called the Sea Grant Programs. "In 1963 about 400 boats foundered on uncharted rocks, or because pilots couldn't comprehend the charts. Another 400 capsized in storms, emphasizing our ignorance about weather."

Mr. Abel anticipates proposals for applied research from colleges, universities, and other institutions. Authorized by Congress in 1966 and administered by the National Science Foundation, Sea Grant Programs will foster "the development and beneficial exploitation of marine resources" through training, research, and advisory services. The first grants will be given in 1967, and qualified institutions eventually will receive "Sea Grant College" status.

"Athelstan Spilhaus, Dean of the University of Minnesota's Institute of Technology, conceived the basic Sea Grant College idea in 1963," Mr. Abel said. "He took his cue from Land Grant Colleges, established by Congress over a century ago, which encourage scholars to tackle practical agricultural problems in conjunction with the work of basic scientists. That way research discoveries are swiftly put to use."

Dean Spilhaus envisions "county agents in hip boots" sharing sea-grant findings with men on trawlers, drilling rigs, and merchant ships. "We'll put ideas to the critical test," Mr. Abel said, "in the only laboratory that can give us the answers — the sea itself."

Oil production platform stands on stilts in the Gulf of Mexico, linked to the mainland by a radio tower and heliport. Burning waste flares above the installation. Such rigs can draw petroleum from dozens of underwater wells.

9

Homes in the Sea

BY JAMES DUGAN

Home for oceanauts, Deep Cabin, a part of Cousteau's Conshelf experiments, rests in the Red Sea 90 feet down. Bottles of breathing gas ring the experimental two-man capsule. Here technicians position floodlights for photographers.

ON A RAW DECEMBER day in 1966 I was having a plate of Whitstable oysters in a London club when my companion, architect Alexander Flinder, pulled a small magazine from his pocket. It was *Triton,* journal of the British Sub-Aqua Club. "Jim," Alex said, pointing to a classified advertisement, "here's the perfect hideaway for you."

Underwater House for hire or sale, operating depth 100 ft. Bournemouth Sub-Aqua Club, 17 Dunbar Road, Bournemouth, Hants.

It wasn't a joke. Only four years after man first occupied an undersea dwelling, any adventurer with the interest and the money to spare could buy one of his own—complete with three portholes, two bunks, and a private bath.

"It's the '*Glaucus,*' first manned station our members made," said Alex, who spends his vacations exploring ancient sunken harbors in the Mediterranean and who also serves as honorary secretary of the BS-AC.

On September 16, 1965, two young British aquanauts, Colin Irwin and John Heath, plunged 35 feet into Plymouth Sound and set up housekeeping for a week in this 12 × 7-foot steel cylinder.

Their submerged home bore the name of the mythical Greek diver who leaped into the sea and found he had become a deity. But Irwin and Heath were in tune with the spirit of today's underwater age. Amateurs with no unusual diving experience, they had joined a new breed of pioneers seeking to live and work in the piercing cold and blinding turbidity, in the surges and currents of the world beneath the waves.

Manned undersea stations (MUST's) are an old dream, but any thought of building and occupying them had to wait until man devised a way to live underwater.

Late one night in September, 1959, I sat in my Manhattan apartment with two of the first men to prove that man could, indeed, work, eat, and sleep underwater—Captains Bond and Cousteau.

Before entering the U. S. Navy, George Bond had served as a country doctor and part-time lay preacher in the tiny mountain community of Bat Cave, North Carolina.

There he won acclaim as a jeep-riding general practitioner, the only doctor for some 6,000 people in a 400-square-mile area. A different kind of fame awaited him in the Navy. Beginning with record-breaking test escapes from bottomed submarines and sinking jet aircraft, he expanded his interests to include undersea living.

We were all agreed that man should have the capacity to live and work freely on the ocean bottom. Cousteau and I listened with mounting excitement as George explained his idea of how this might be done—a concept based on the process of saturation.

"Give a diver a certain amount of compressed breathing gases at a given depth," George said, "and his body will become completely saturated with the mixture. At that point, the pressure of the dissolved gases in his tissues and his blood will match the pressure of the gas he's breathing."

George told us of tank experiments with Navy divers using the rare light gas helium which, unlike the nitrogen in the air we breathe, does not cause narcosis. He and two fellow workers, Capt. Walter F. Mazzone and Capt. Robert D. Workman, confirmed that after 30 hours at any depth of water the body reaches the limit of its capacity for absorbing this innocuous gas.

"Once the body tissues are saturated with the gas breathed at any depth, and as long as the pressure inside an undersea station equals the pressure outside, a diver can move in and out freely," George explained. "And on his return to the surface, the time required to free him of absorbed gases through decompression remains the same —no matter how long he stays down. Depending, of course, on the depth of the saturation exposure, a diver generally can be brought up at a rate of six feet per hour.

"The time underwater is no longer a factor; only depth determines the length of decompression. This is the big gain of saturation diving, and it means we can keep a diver down for days, weeks, or months, instead of minutes."

This great time-saving idea, so casually described by George, became the basis of seven major efforts to settle man undersea for increasing lengths of time—Cousteau's three Conshelf experiments, Link's two Man-in-Sea projects, and the U. S. Navy's two Sealab programs.

Almost simultaneously, Cousteau and Link began to attack the problem of prolonging man's activities underwater, and in

JERRY GREENBERG

Seated in an anchored rubber tube, Floridian Edmond L. Fisher spends a sleepless night during the first endurance test with scuba in July, 1954. Every hour for 24 hours, an assistant swam 30 feet down to him with a replacement air tank. At right Fisher unfolds a kit containing food and fresh water plus a hammer and chisel for collecting coral from Florida's French Reef.

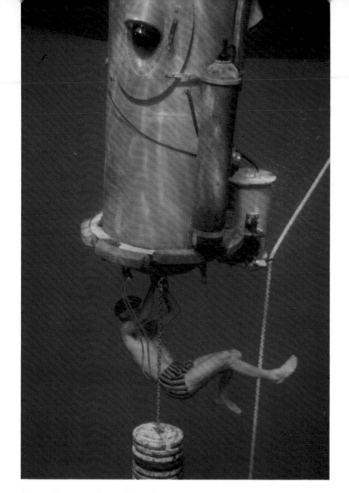

Entering a submersible decompression chamber, Jon Lindbergh, son of the famous flyer, prepares for a descent of 432 feet off Great Stirrup Cay in the Bahamas. The line leads to an inflated rubber dwelling, the SPID, where underwater pioneers Lindbergh and Robert Sténuit remained for two days beyond the reach of divers from the surface. At right, a hoist lifts the chamber back aboard Edwin A. Link's research vessel Sea Diver. *Below, Annie Sténuit smiles at her husband through the porthole of a deck decompression chamber.*

September, 1962, my wife Ruth and I went to the south of France to cover these first historic attempts.

From *Sea Diver,* Link tested the first stage of a long-range experiment to use three major pieces of equipment — a submersible decompression chamber; a submersible portable inflatable dwelling (SPID); and a deck decompression chamber. "The ultimate aim," Link said, "is to enable men to live and work on the floor of the ocean at depths of 1,000 feet or possibly more."

On September 6, the great test came.

While Cousteau completed arrangements to send two men to live in the Mediterranean, Link, only 100 miles away, sent a 29-year-old Belgian diver, Robert Sténuit, into the water off Villefranche-sur-Mer on the French Riviera.

Sténuit swam into the submersible decompression chamber, which also served as a combination underwater elevator and diving bell. The 11 × 3-foot cylinder moved up and down on a chain cable moored to the bottom, and contained two compartments, an instrument-packed main cham-

ber, and an air lock to pass a man in or out.

Once inside the capsule, Sténuit tried to talk by telephone with the men on board *Sea Diver*, but they were unable to understand him because his special breathing mixture of almost pure helium made him sound like a squeaky combination of Donald Duck and Popeye.

He reached 200 feet and stopped the capsule 43 feet above the flat, muddy bottom. Several times he went outside, free as a fish, to simulate work and once to fetch his dinner from a lowered canister. During

185

the night he felt very cold and slept sitting up, resting his head on a shelf table. At noon the next day, the phone rang. "Robert," said Ed Link, "the *mistral* came up this morning, heavy seas are rising. Don't worry if you are a little shaken up."

Then, half an hour later, came an order from Lt. Comdr. Robert C. Bornmann, USN, the project physician, "Winch up to 100 feet."

"But why?" asked Sténuit, who was ready to try for a 48-hour dive. Bornmann replied, "We seem to be using a little more helium than anticipated. There have been a few leaks up here, and with this wind . . . we'll have to wait for the evening lull to take you back on board. There isn't enough helium to wait until tomorrow night, so we must do it tonight."

Disappointed, Sténuit obeyed the order,

pressing the winch control button in the capsule. After 24 hours and 15 minutes underwater, he was hauled aboard the rolling ship—the first man to prove in the open sea the feasibility of manned stations and saturation diving.

Someone passed a copy of the London *Daily Mail* to Sténuit while he was decompressing. Only then did he learn the real reason for his shortened stay:

. . . Robert Sténuit was brought to the surface late tonight. . . . not knowing his life was in grave danger. He had not been told that a boat bringing supplies . . . sank in heavy seas. . . . It carried 15 containers of the precious helium gas that Sténuit needs. . . . Sténuit . . . is talking . . . in a still-distorted voice. It sounds like Popeye's, . . . the effect of helium on the vocal cords.

Only four days after Sténuit emerged from the chamber, Ruth and I stood with

dozens of others aboard Cousteau's *Calypso* as Albert Falco and Claude Wesly dived 33 feet down off the coast near Marseille to the first true sea house, Conshelf One.

Cousteau had set up an elaborate, doubly secured operation with a 60-man supporting team on the surface. He feared that ships might be blown about in the stormy mistral season. So he strung the undersea station's lines for air, power, water, telephone, and television along the bottom to a headquarters ashore. Each system had a duplicate in reserve in case of failure.

Falco called the habitat "Diogenes," after the Greek philosopher who lived in a tub. A 17 × 8-foot cylindrical steel workshop filled with compressed air, the station was heavily weighted and anchored to the bottom. Television monitors allowed topside scientists and technicians to observe Falco and Wesly.

Heedless of a swimmer feeding surgeonfish outside, oceanauts play chess in Cousteau's Conshelf Two. The steel Starfish House (below) sheltered five men for a month on a ledge 36 feet down in the Red Sea. At lower right, the diving saucer eases through the bottom of its air-filled hangar.

Each day the oceanauts exited through an open hatch and sortied with Aqua-Lungs for as long as five hours at a time to a maximum depth of 85 feet. Doctors came down twice a day to examine them, and divers brought mail, newspapers, hot food —sealed in pressure cookers.

Falco and Wesly had opened the station in high spirits, but on the third day a change came over them. "I feel small," Falco wrote in his log. "I have to go slowly, otherwise I'll never make it. I'm afraid I can't hold out. The work in the water becomes terribly hard. Everything is getting too difficult."

On the fourth day, Cousteau limited visits from the surface and morale improved. "It's more peaceful now . . . ," Falco wrote. "I now believe that life under the sea for a long period in greater depths is possible. But, what if one should completely forget the earth? When I think about that, I realize I simply don't care what's going on up there. Claude feels the same."

Cousteau himself swam down to visit the oceanauts, and observed that concepts of "inside" and "outside" were fading away. "Falco and Wesly passed from air to water and water to air with insouciance, as if the antagonisms of the elements had been abolished," he wrote later. Cousteau called them

Capturing marine life in plastic bags and on film in the Red Sea, French oceanauts move weightlessly in a medium 800 times heavier than air. Transparent cages, buoyed by air bubbles, hold fish for transfer to underwater stock pens. From there a biologist sent some by air to the Aquarium at Monaco. Large rudderfish swirl beside the flooded toolshed of an undersea hamlet, Conshelf Two, where seven men worked during a month-long experiment in sea-floor habitation. Project leader Cousteau (far right) steadies a camera for a scene in his motion picture World Without Sun. *Since 1952, the National Geographic Society has helped support his work.*

ROBERT GOODMAN

bearers of marvelous news, "that a species of man would come—men-of-the-water, creatures of inner space. . . ."

Ruth and I stood amid the expectant crowd when the oceanauts surfaced after 169 hours and 13 minutes. As soon as Wesly returned to the tender, he told Cousteau, "I'm ready to start again, Commandant—this time longer and deeper."

And within a year he had his wish. He became the first man to live in two undersea houses. In June, 1963, he joined six other divers in a much more ambitious venture, Conshelf Two.

This time Cousteau chose a site 36 feet down in the Red Sea, the remote Sha'ab Rumi, or "Roman Reef," near Port Sudan. Instead of a single ocean dwelling, he designed a small colony—two steel "houses," a hangar for the diving saucer, a tool shed, fish pens, and anti-shark cages. Five men lived for a month in the command center, an assembly of four cylindrical chambers radiating in a design that suggested the structure's name, Starfish House.

Oceanaut Pierre Vannoni, a meticulous ex-customs inspector, kept an informal log he entitled, "What It Is Like to Live and Work Inside the Sea." He wrote of scrubbing away algae and shellfish that coated the structures, of experiments to see if color attracted fish, and of the odd appearance of the men who came down to see them. "Day by day we notice that our visitors are losing weight and getting rings under their eyes," Vannoni wrote. "The effort demanded from everyone above is enormous. We follow all this from our sunken castle as powerless onlookers, rosy and plump, idle and pampered."

Cousteau told me he chose these oceanauts not as underwater athletes, but rather for skills they had displayed on land. For example, the bearded chef, Pierre ("Pierrot") Guilbert, 43, had mild arteriosclerosis, but he went down and cooked. A 15-inch

triggerfish "adopted" ·the chef when he obligingly opened a clam for it. After that, the fish unerringly distinguished him from the other masked oceanauts. Pierrot summoned his pet by rapping on the window, and the fish would thrust its head through the diving hatch to grab table scraps. When dinner was late, the fish impatiently flipped water into the house.

Professor Raymond Vaissière, 38, chief of the biological division of the Oceanographic Museum at Monaco, also had little diving experience, but he became the first scientist to enjoy his own undersea laboratory. Cousteau said he thought that ocean scientists of the past would have turned

"sea-green with envy" over "our Professor Vaissière's privilege of spending a lordly month" in the fishes' habitat with his own collecting staff, underwater cameras, stock pens, and field laboratory.

Near Starfish House, on a huge tripod, stood a pressurized onion-shaped dome, the underwater hangar for the diving saucer. Many times Falco maneuvered the craft through a hatch into the sea. He also carried visiting scientists 900 feet down. For the first time, a submarine was operating from an underwater base!

On the outskirts of the sea-bottom village, 54 feet farther down, two men lived and worked for a week in Deep Cabin, an

JERRY GREENBERG (ABOVE) AND ELGIN CIAMPI

"Papa Topside," U. S. Navy divers affectionately call Capt. George F. Bond, who pioneered the concept that men could live and work undersea.

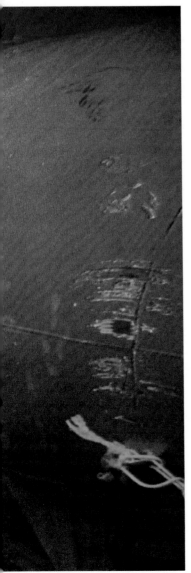

Hungry greater amberjacks gobble bits of sardine fed them from the "back porch" of Sealab I, the U. S. Navy's first undersea habitat. In the summer of 1964, four divers lived here almost 11 days, their only connection to the surface a cable for water, power, and communications. At left, an aquanaut swims past portholes of the chamber, bottomed at 193 feet off Bermuda.

11-foot-high rocket-shaped chamber. From the bottom hatch they went out daily to work in 165 feet of water, and sometimes took excursion dives to 330 feet and more.

In June of 1964, just a year after the men of Conshelf Two had surfaced, Ed Link prepared for the deepest stay ever, phase two of Man-in-Sea. His submersible decompression chamber had an important role to play, and for this experiment he would inhabit the continental shelf in a house of inflated rubber, the SPID. Link was convinced that heavy walls were unnecessary for a successful submarine habitat. He knew the structure would not collapse if pressure inside equaled pressure outside. And for more than a year he had collaborated with Dr. C. J. Lambertsen of the University of Pennsylvania's Department of Pharmacology in developing critically important environmental and life support systems.

But this time the doctors had two men to watch over, for Robert Sténuit had a companion, Jon Lindbergh, son of the famous flyer and a highly experienced, resourceful underwater engineer. They would be on their own 432 feet down in the Bahamas off

Astronaut-aquanaut, Navy Comdr. M. Scott Carpenter reviews the plan of the day in Sealab II, where he spent 30 days at a depth of 205 feet. Home to three alternating teams, the station (below) bobs off La Jolla, California, before descending to the sea floor. On the support vessel (opposite), a crane raises the personnel transport capsule, an "elevator" from the deep.

RON CHURCH (BELOW) AND U. S. NAVY

Checkered sphere of Conshelf Three hangs from cables in Nice Harbor, ready for its first underwater test off nearby Monaco. The steel globe rests on a chassis that holds 77 tons of ballast. Later, it became a home for six oceanauts 328 feet down in the Mediterranean. While living underwater, the men breathed "heliox"—a mixture of about 98 percent helium and 2 percent oxygen. Captain Cousteau (below) tightens a heliox regulator hose in a predive test.

Great Stirrup Cay, beyond reach of divers.

On June 30, Sténuit and Lindbergh descended in the decompression chamber, which they left anchored near the SPID for the trip back. "The gas of the interior tastes like fresh mountain air," Sténuit said of the moment the pair entered their new home, an 8 × 4-foot tent that looked somewhat like a large sausage. "At last, at last, I am here. Six months of delays, of dogged effort, but now I am here. What calm there is in this other world. What silence. What peace."

Since helium causes a much greater body-heat loss than nitrogen, the aquanauts shivered in many layers of wool clothing despite an inside temperature of 76° F.

The divers dined on carrot juice, corned beef, canned water, and fruit salad, all from pressure-dented cans. Through the first night they alternated standing watch and sleeping poorly. Next morning they swam out to the end of their 50-foot gas hoses. The drab floor teemed with life. A scavenging grouper, possibly weighing 200 pounds, tugged at their swimfins and then held still while they stroked it.

In the afternoon the voice of Ed Link came through on the intercom, "May I

NATIONAL GEOGRAPHIC PHOTOGRAPHER BATES W. LITTLEHALES

congratulate you for being the first men to have lived a whole day at 432 feet depth." Jon sent telegrams to his four children in Santa Barbara, California. "We are in a small rubber house on the bottom of the ocean," he said in one. "Hundreds of little fish are swimming outside the window. . . . Two . . . octopuses were playing on the bottom under us yesterday. They would glide into a hole and then jump out at the fish."

At night sardines danced in the open diving well, chasing crustaceans and larvae in the glare of the interior light. Something hit the SPID a heavy blow and its occupants

held onto their bunks as the station rocked. The big grouper had charged the sardines, slamming into the open hatch. He shook the station ten times during the night as he chased his prey.

On the second day Sténuit tested an emergency communications system for use if intercom and telegraph failed. He slipped messages into plastic bottles and released them to soar aloft. Barracuda, amberjack, and king mackerel hit the bottles but disdained to swallow them.

Ed Link phoned again: "Robert and Jon, you have spent two days and two nights at

195

432 feet, and all our tests have succeeded. Bravo! . . . We'll gain nothing more by extending your stay. . . . Get ready to come up."

Once the submersible chamber reached the deck of *Sea Diver*, the crew coupled it with the large deck decompression chamber and Robert and Jon transferred to enjoy in comfort the first of several steak dinners. For nearly four days they stayed in the chamber until their bodies adjusted to normal atmospheric pressure. But they regarded their confinement as a small price to pay for success. Had they stayed down two weeks or even two months, their decompression time would have been the same.

A month after Sténuit and Lindbergh emerged, Captain Bond had completed preparations to supervise the first U.S. Navy undersea station. On July 18, he gave the order to lower a prototype 40 × 9-foot steel cylinder to a depth of 193 feet southwest of Bermuda.

Two days later four Navy divers—a doctor and three enlisted men—entered a small submersible decompression chamber and descended for two minutes to reach Sealab I. Inside the cylinder they settled down in quarters tied to the surface only by a power, water, and communications cable. "We are doing fine," the aquanauts reported. "It is nice and comfortable down here. We could stay forever."

On the second day the men began a work program of embedding ultrasonic beacons in the ocean floor as direction finders; making films, photographs, and sound recordings; and installing acoustic devices and electric lights to determine their effect on sharks. But no sharks appeared.

The sixth day, a Sunday, Sealab I became a chapel for a service of thanksgiving and hymn singing. Early on the eleventh day, the men entered their submersible

Floating on the job, technicians 370 feet down repair a five-ton "Christmas tree," an assembly of tubes and valves that simulates an underwater oil well. Wielding tools made lighter by the water's buoyancy, the divers demonstrated that men can manipulate heavy equipment in the depths.

PHILIPPE COUSTEAU

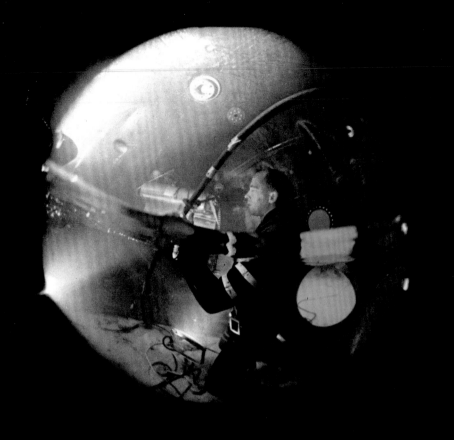

Shoulder-deep in water, a diver kneels on the sea floor inside Link's rubber Igloo, forcing the water out with compressed air from a hose. When inflated, the weighted dome (below) provides a dry work space. The submarino Deep Diver shuttles men 50 feet to the surface near Grand Bahama Island. A submersible portable inflatable dwelling (SPID) at right contains bunks so divers can stay overnight, entering through the bottom hatch.

NATIONAL GEOGRAPHIC PHOTOGRAPHER BATES W. LITTLEHALES (RIGHT) AND JERRY GREENBERG

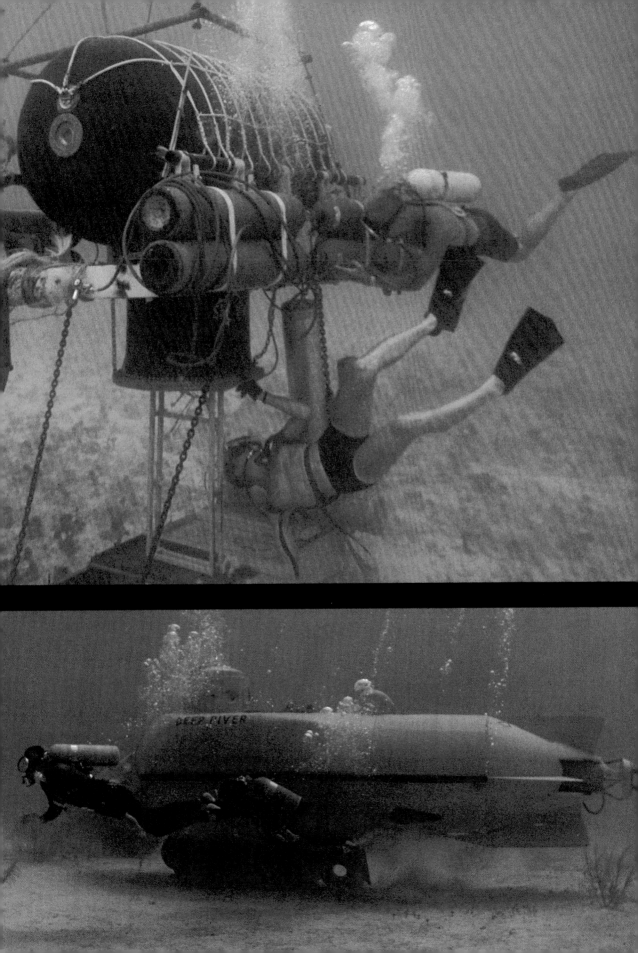

decompression chamber for the trip back to the surface.

Later, the Navy authorized a full man-in-the-sea project, with George as principal investigator. Plans for Sealab II were put into effect, and from August 10 to October 12, 1965, he supervised the longest and most ambitious manned undersea experiment ever conducted. This time, the cylinder—57 feet long and 12 feet in diameter—could accommodate ten aquanauts.

The site lay 205 feet down, a mile out in the Pacific from the Scripps Institution of Oceanography. Twenty-eight divers in three teams occupied Sealab II in 15-day segments for 45 days. Among them was M. Scott Carpenter, then an astronaut-aquanaut, on loan from the National Aeronautics and Space Administration.

Around Sealab II the water was 50° F. or less, and silt covered the bottom. One area of deep sediment the divers called the "Black Hole of Calcutta." At times, clouds of plankton and mud reduced visibility to six inches. "Most of our work will be done in such conditions," George said, "rather than in clear waters like those off Bermuda."

The key word in Sealab II was work, and the men frequently found it necessary to schedule dives, keep the log, cook, communicate, and clean up, all at the same time.

But the team had the help of a real underwater expert, Tuffy, a trained porpoise fitted with a harness. Once he dived 200 feet to the house and back seven times in 20 minutes, delivering mail and supplies. Tuffy also demonstrated how he could help rescue an aquanaut in trouble. On hearing a buzzer from the surface, he swam to a "rescue diver" who hooked a line onto the harness. Tuffy whipped away, swiftly carrying the guideline to the "distressed man."

By coincidence, while the men of Sealab II performed in the Pacific, Cousteau's oceanauts were living and working in Conshelf Three in the Mediterranean. When I visited the French site in the diving saucer, I saw the oceanauts swimming around a stack of pipes and valves known as a "Christmas tree," an assembly for control-

ling the flow of crude oil from undersea wells. On land truckborne specialists repair wellheads, but on the sea floor divers must maintain them. No drill hole bored downward under the experimental wellhead at Conshelf Three. Instead compressed air simulated the force of a real well.

For seven aching hours one oceanaut worked to thread a stiff wire through a thick pack of pressure-proof seals, completing a wellhead repair that many oil technicians had thought impossible underwater. On shore, skeptical engineers watching on TV monitors applauded as a crew of divers attached a 400-pound repair assembly to the wellhead in record time.

The day before my voyage in the diving saucer I had joined Cousteau in the Oceanographic Museum at Monaco to listen to the first interoceanic telephone call. The French oceanauts of Conshelf Three rang up the American aquanauts of Sealab II, 6,000 miles away.

Through the static and the confusion of language the men traded nothing of scientific importance, but they shared a new comradeship of the deep. No matter how many TV and telephone links they had with the surface, they felt detached from the world above. They lived in strange houses, breathing exotic gas mixtures and working in a dark and eerie netherworld. And together—as pioneers of the deep frontier—they faced a challenge almost as immense as that of the conquest of space.

Man has planted his footsteps in the underwater realm that for centuries caused all but a venturesome few to tremble. Now, if he is truly to make the sea his own, he must act with care and judgment. He may exploit and ravage this new world as he has the land, or he may by careful conservation make of it a self-renewing source of countless benefits. The choice is his.

"Moon walk" on the sea floor: Working to expand man's knowledge of space, an engineer in a suit worn by astronauts crosses a Virgin Islands seascape that simulates the light gravity of the lunar environment. The back pack supplies breathing gas, and the staff helps steady him.

Acknowledgements

The Special Publications Division is grateful to the consultants and authorities named or quoted in the text and to those listed here, for their generous cooperation and assistance during the preparation of this book.

Mrs. James Dugan; Dr. Leonard P. Schultz, Senior Zoologist, Miss Maureen E. Downey, Division of Echinoderms, and Mendel Peterson, Museum of History and Technology, all Smithsonian Institution; Richard Vetter, Executive Secretary, Committee on Oceanography, and Lee M. Hunt, Executive Secretary, Mine Advisory Committee, both National Academy of Sciences.

Dr. Edward Wenk, Jr., Executive Secretary, National Council on Marine Resources and Engineering Development; Haven Emerson, Vice President, Sanford Marine Services; Gordon Kazanjian, Director, Marketing Division, Ocean Systems, Inc.; Lt. Comdr. C. W. Larson II, Public Affairs Officer, and Norman Hanson, Assistant PAO, Deep Submergence Systems Project, U. S. Navy; Russell Greenbaum, Head, Public Affairs, Office of Naval Research; Richard Vahan, Assistant Curator, New England Aquarium.

William S. Glidden, Marine Biologist, and Larry K. Hawkins, Oceanographer, both Naval Oceanographic Office; O. L. Wallis, Aquatic Resources Biologist, and Fred M. Packard, International Specialist, both National Park Service; Comdr. William R. Leibold and Lt. Comdr. John Harter, both Navy Experimental Diving Unit; Richard A. Waller, Biologist, Bureau of Commercial Fisheries; Dr. Russell Keim, Executive Secretary, Committee on Ocean Engineering, National Academy of Engineering; and Ord Alexander, Underwater Engineering Consultant.

Additional References

Oceanography and the sea in general: Robert C. Cowen, *Frontiers of the Sea;* George R. Deacon, ed., *Seas, Maps, and Men;* Rhodes W. Fairbridge, ed., *Encyclopedia of Oceanography;* Sir William Herdman, *Founders of Oceanography and Their Work;* Matthew Fontaine Maury, *The Physical Geography of the Sea and Its Meteorology;* Robert C. Miller, *The Sea;* Claiborne Pell with Harold Goodwin, *Challenge of the Seven Seas;* Sir Charles Thomson, *The Voyage of the Challenger,* Vols. I and II; Hein Wenzel, *The Sea.*

Life in the sea: Rachel Carson, *The Edge of the Sea;* William J. Cromie, *The Living World of the Sea;* Clarence Idyll, *Abyss: The Deep Sea and the Creatures that Live in It;* National Geographic Society, *Wondrous World of Fishes.*

Marine archeology and treasure: George F. Bass, *Archaeology Under Water;* Honor Frost, *Under the Mediterranean;* Marion C. Link, *Sea Diver;* Joan du Plat Taylor, ed., *Marine Archaeology;* Peter Throckmorton, *The Lost Ships;* Kip Wagner as told to L. B. Taylor, Jr., *Pieces of Eight.*

Diving: Capt. Jacques-Yves Cousteau and James Dugan, *The Living Sea;* Capt. Jacques-Yves Cousteau with Frédéric Dumas, *The Silent World;* Robert H. Davis, *Deep Diving and Submarine Operations;* James Dugan, *Man Under the Sea;* Guy Gilpatric, *The Compleat Goggler;* Pierre de Latil and Jean Rivoire, *Man and the Underwater World;* Owen Lee, *The Complete Illustrated Guide to Snorkel and Deep Diving;* Robert Sténuit, *The Deepest Days.*

Bathyspheres, bathyscaphs, and submarines: William Beebe, *Half Mile Down;* Jacques Piccard and Robert S. Dietz, *Seven Miles Down;* Wilbur Cross, *Challengers of the Deep.*

For additional reading on the world beneath the sea, you may wish to refer to the following NATIONAL GEOGRAPHIC articles and to check the Cumulative Index for related material.

George F. Bass: "Underwater Archeology: Key to History's Warehouse," July, 1963. Capt. Jacques-Yves Cousteau: "Working for Weeks on the Sea Floor," Apr., 1966; "At Home in the Sea," Apr., 1964; "Diving Saucer Takes to the Deep," Apr., 1960; "Diving Through an Undersea Avalanche," Apr., 1955; "Fish Men Discover a 2,200-Year Old Greek Ship," Jan., 1954. Dr. Harold E. Edgerton: "Photographing the Sea's Dark Underworld," Apr., 1955. Maurice Ewing: "New Discoveries on the Mid-Atlantic Ridge," Nov., 1949. Anders Franzén: "Ghost From the Depths: the Warship *Vasa,*" Jan., 1962. Edwin I. Griffin: "Making Friends with a Killer Whale," Mar., 1966. Lt. Comdr. Georges S. Houot: "Two and a Half Miles Down," July, 1954. Edwin A. Link: "Outpost Under the Ocean," Apr., 1965; "Tomorrow on the Deep Frontier," June, 1964; "Our Man-in-Sea Project," May, 1963. Marion C. Link: "Exploring the Drowned City of Port Royal," Feb., 1960. Luis Marden: "Camera Under the Sea," Feb., 1956. Samuel W. Matthews: "Science Explores the Monsoon Sea," Oct., 1967. Jacques Piccard: "Man's Deepest Dive," Aug., 1960. Carleton Ray: "Stalking Seals Under Antarctic Ice," Jan., 1966. Walter A. Starck II: "Marvels of a Coral Realm," Nov., 1966. Robert Sténuit: "The Deepest Days," Apr., 1965. Peter Throckmorton: "Oldest Known Shipwreck Yields Bronze Age Cargo," May, 1962; "Thirty-three Centuries Under the Sea," May, 1960. Kip Wagner: "Drowned Galleons Yield Spanish Gold," Jan., 1965; Robert Schroeder: "Alligator Reef," Jan., 1964.

Index

Illustrations page references appear in *italics.*

Composition by National Geographic's Phototypographic Division,
Herman J.A.C. Arens, Director; John E. McConnell, Manager.
Printed and bound by Fawcett-Haynes Printing Corporation, Rockville, Md.
Color separations by Lanman Engraving Company, Alexandria, Va.; Beck Engraving
Company, Philadelphia, Pa.; and Graphic Color Plate, Inc., Stamford, Conn.